Oxford

FAMOUS for its prestigious university, Oxford has so much more than "dreaming spires" to enjoy, as Victorian poet Matthew Arnold famously wrote. It has first class museums, displaying everything from a blackboard used by Albert Einstein through to internationally significant collections that will transport you right back in time.

Stephen Hawking and actor Hugh Laurie hail from Oxford and if the city seems familiar, perhaps it's thanks to the TV series "Inspector Morse", much of which was filmed in this architecturally stunning city. Talk about drop dead gorgeous!

If you want to look at things from a different angle, you could always take to the river and hire a punt or a rowing boat from Folly Bridge, Magdalen Bridge or Cherwell Boathouse. ■

3

Contents

Dear Readers . . .

I'm delighted to welcome you to "The People's Friend" Annual 2019. Its 176 pages are packed with hours of feel-good reading, with 25 heartwarming new short stories written by some of your favourite authors and accompanied by beautiful colour illustrations.

We've included a selection of seasonal poems to suit every mood and occasion, 10 glorious watercolour paintings from the brush of J. Campbell Kerr, and fascinating facts and figures on how our world was changing in 1869, when the "Friend" first launched.

I do hope you enjoy reading it all!

Angela

Angela Gilchrist, Editor

Complete Stories

p42

Poetry

J. Campbell Kerr Paintings

Our Changing World

A House Of Dreams

by Sally Trueman Dicken

I **OPEN** my eyes in an unfamiliar room, bathed in sunlight. Luke is still sleeping, so I give him a shake. It's our house-hunting weekend away. "Hey, sleepy-head, wake up. We've a busy day in front of us. That bed might be super comfy, but we have to fit in as many house viewings as possible today."

Luke opens one eye and shuts it quickly.

"You go and have a shower, Jessy. I'll be awake by the time you have finished."

"Oh, no, you don't. You'll go back to sleep, and you know we need to find a new home as soon as we can. I need to get the nursery ready if nothing else."

I have to be motivated for both of us. It's hard sometimes, because Luke has such a sunny, laid-back personality that he doesn't always grasp the urgency of the situation.

Please let today be the day that we find our perfect home. There's not a lot of time left. Our baby will be here in December. I stroke my barely visible bump to reassure William that all will be well.

Luke's new job entails a move from one side of the country to the other. If we are not successful today, it may mean living in rented accommodation for a while or being separated, which would be unthinkable.

The houses we have looked at so far have been no good at all. There was one very modern property that I fell in love with, but the owners are not ready to sell yet – they were only trying out the market. Why do people do that?

We have a list of properties to view, but somehow I don't feel hopeful.

My mobile sings out with a call from the estate agent.

"Hi, there, it's Darren here from New Homes. Exciting news. Forget the list for a moment, I have a wild card – a property just come on the market this morning. It doesn't fit your specifications exactly but it's worth a viewing."

I shake Luke's shoulder again and press the speaker button.

"It needs a complete makeover, but there's bags of potential. No details on the website yet. I know you said modern and ready to move into as soon as possible, with no decorating to do, but this is a real bargain. Are you interested in a viewing?"

Illustration by Sarah Holliday.

"Let's just take a look," I say to Luke. "It can't hurt to see what it's like. "

I spot the estate agent as we draw up to the kerb. Smart and nonchalant, he lolls against his car, chatting into his iPhone.

He looks barely out of school, energetic, smartly dressed, wearing shoes that have absurdly long toes, his gelled hair styled into peaks like the royal icing on traditional Christmas cakes.

I can sense his disguised frustration at being unable to make a sale. He seemed pleased when we had liked the modern town house, completely renovated, gleaming with fresh white paint throughout, but now his manner is not so confident.

"Why did you agree to look at this house, when we both agreed we wanted modern?" Luke hisses as we stand outside the property.

"Wait and see," I whisper, leaning so close that I brush his cheek with mine. The familiar aroma of his aftershave seems comforting, reassuring me.

The house must have been beautiful once: an Edwardian villa with walls constructed of dark blue pennant stone, with beige sandstone trims.

It has tall bay windows, top and bottom; their sash frames, once elegant, are now grubby, badly in need of a coat of paint.

"This house is just like a genteel old lady, once attractive, now in reduced

7

circumstances," I say. Luke merely shrugs his shoulders.

We watch as our agent wrestles with his key in the lock, then pushes the door open, revealing an elaborate mosaic floor of brown, white and black tiles in the hall.

"Very pretty." I gasp with surprise.

We follow him into the dim hallway where dust motes rise to dance in the sunlight. I shiver and sneeze.

Moving from room to room, we say little. There are oak floorboards underfoot with the odd patch of patterned carpet here and there; a reminder of happy days when the house was a family home, full of people.

"It needs a lot of work," I mutter.

"You're not joking." Luke reaches for my hand.

"Please don't try to open those." The estate agent's face is full of alarm as Luke tries to raise one of the sash windows. "Most of the cords are broken. They would be absolutely lethal if they came crashing down."

We climb the stairs with care; a mottled carpet ragged at the edges, secured with brass stair rods, now black with age, threatens to trip us with every step.

An old toy lies on the floor of the smallest bedroom. I walk over to pick it up. A little fluffy lamb, obviously once much-loved, makes me visualise a cot in the corner, a newly decorated room, nursery curtains.

Downstairs once more, we tiptoe through the wreck of a kitchen and into the breakfast room to look at the garden through the French windows.

"I thought it best to view the garden from here," the agent is saying. "It needs quite a considerable amount of work to tame that jungle."

We gaze, hand in hand, at the spiralling brambles and tottering lavender bushes entwined with lush green goose grass.

"A tiger could live in there," Luke says.

"A whole pack of them," I agree.

"May I point out," the estate agent says, bravely trying to make a sale, "that the garden is huge. There is a back entrance to the lane with plenty of room for a garage and workshops."

"Interesting," I say politely.

I glance across at Luke. There is no need to speak. This house would mean too much work for us. Renovation would keep us busy day and night, for we would not be able to afford to hire in builders and decorators after taking on a large mortgage. It is way beyond our capabilities.

The last room to be inspected makes our spirits sink even lower. The sun has gone behind a cloud. The room looks incredibly dingy and forlorn.

We turn to the agent, impatiently tapping one of his immaculate shoes on the dusty oak floorboards.

Luke starts to speak to release him from his misery.

"We think . . ."

And then it happens.

The sun comes out from behind the clouds, shining through the grimy glass, breaking through the gloom with its brilliant rays, as if someone has flicked a switch somewhere.

Sunlight, streaming through cut-glass diamond shapes in the leaded windows, decorates the carpet with orbs of red, blue and green.

Prisms dangling from the ceiling split the same light into rainbows, on the walls, on the old furniture and on a very beautiful fireplace previously unnoticed behind us.

"Oh, look!" I gasp. "It's an Arts and Crafts fireplace." My fingers trace the whorls on the elaborate carved oak mantelpiece. "It's beautiful."

"We could rescue this house," Luke says, half to himself.

I know what he is dreaming of: his grandad's workshop, a special place in his childhood, with rows of gleaming tools on hooks next to jars of screws and nails, all methodically arranged and labelled.

My visions are of the kitchen restored to a proper working space. It makes me think of all those cookery programmes on television. I see myself making jam tarts with a toddler helping me roll out pastry.

My imagination begins to work overtime. I picture myself in an apron like Nana, beating eggs into a swirling yellow froth in one of those old-fashioned earthenware bowls she used to perch on her hip. How those eggs didn't spill out was one of life's mysteries.

This is a house full of dreams. It is certainly worth some serious consideration. I shiver, shaking my head to return to reality.

"What do you think, Jessica?" Luke asks, coming to stand next to me once more, seeking my hand.

I turn to face him.

"You could make this place into the most wonderful home. Some of the features are brilliant and there is plenty of room for improvement.

"That garden outside gives lots of scope for a garage, workshops, sun house and even a huge conservatory."

"Are you tempted, then, Jessy? I don't really understand. You always said you wanted a more modern place, like the one we looked at yesterday; the one that took your breath away."

I hesitate before speaking.

"I can see the potential in it now the sun has come out, and if I was interested in old houses, I would say yes in a heartbeat." I pause. "But . . . no, I don't want to buy it."

The estate agent sighs, and sidles off towards the front door. I smile at Luke's bewildered face and continue.

"However, I do know someone who would like to buy it: the man selling the wonderful modern house we looked at yesterday.

"When you were upstairs inspecting the bedrooms with the wife, the owner told me that they wouldn't be selling that house until he found a new project.

"That's why I agreed to come and look at this house when it was so far away from our specifications."

Luke's face is still showing total bemusement.

"Just take a guess at what his new project could be. He is looking for an older property with period features needing lots of attention, at the right price with room to put up some workshops.

"This house would be ideal for them, just waiting for someone to come along to restore it to its former glory."

A gleam of understanding flits across Luke's face.

"Can't you feel the magic of it? I got caught up in it. It even had me dreaming of a kitchen full of copper pans and a big kitchen range, despite the fact I have trouble baking a sponge. I saw you going into a kind of trance at one stage."

Luke looks thoughtful, fingering his beard.

"I was thinking of Grandad's workshop. You're right. This house draws you in. But it wouldn't suit our lifestyle at the moment. It needs a complete makeover."

"But . . ." I wave my arms excitedly ". . . this would suit that family just fine. The husband is itching to get his hands on a house like this one.

"If we can persuade him to put in an offer quickly, then we can put in an offer for his gorgeous newly decorated property."

Just then our baby gives a tentative kick as if he approves of his mum's idea.

"Let's go and phone them now. Let's do it right now before anybody else gets to see the details on the website.

"Let's tell him we have found his dream house. And please would he sell us our dream house."

*　*　*　*

Christmas Day dawns in our brand-new home. We have been awake most of the night with little William bawling with colic. We sit, bleary-eyed, sipping coffee, and gaze at the Christmas tree still awaiting its decorations.

A single string of fairy lights is draped haphazardly over the branches but they shine with warmth against those wonderful white walls.

I have managed to get two presents under the tree: one for Luke and one for William. Luke has yet to wrap mine. Gone are the days of elaborate preparations for the festive season, a pantry full of food and myriad bottles of multicoloured wines.

But we have all we need or would want, here in this room. It's true what they say: home is where the heart is and my heart lies here with my two boys. ∎

Illustration by Gerard Fay.

Happy New Year

by Suzanne Ross Jones

HARRY stirred his tea thoughtfully.

"Do you think tonight's the right time to tell your sister?" he asked, raising his voice just enough to be heard over the chatter and laughter around them.

Victoria's eyes narrowed speculatively and she experienced a brief moment of apprehension. Harry's expression gave nothing away, but then, he wasn't the sort of man to make a fuss – and especially not here in this busy café.

"Have you changed your mind, Harry? About us?"

Her heart fluttered as he reached across the table and took her hand.

"Never," he said with such feeling that she was immediately convinced. "But it's Hogmanay. It's not really the time for springing surprises. And you said you're in the habit of seeing in the bells together, just you and Joanna."

11

"Well, yes." It was true that recently it had been just the two of them, but things had been different once. Victoria smiled at the memory of Hogmanays past; the excitement of the early years, and being allowed by their parents to stay up for the bells; the joy of parties and ceilidhs as they'd grown into teenagers; the cosy New Year's Eve get-togethers, spent with husbands and then children of their own.

The one constant in these celebrations had been Joanna.

One by one, their numbers had diminished. Parents had been lost far too soon. Victoria had been widowed and Joanna divorced. Their families had grown up and started traditions of their own.

Harry frowned.

"I don't want to intrude."

She smiled again. This was one of the reasons she'd fallen in love with Harry – he was so thoughtful.

"Joanna and you and I will make a new habit for Hogmanay. It will be the three of us seeing in the New Year from now on."

"Our news will be a shock for her. We hadn't even met when she went away. What if she thinks we're rushing things?"

Victoria smiled. Joanna and she had often joked that they were too set in their ways for new romances and adventures.

"She won't be expecting it, that's for sure. But she'll be happy for us."

"You're sure?"

"I am. Best way to start the New Year," she told him with a smile. "With all secrets and surprises out in the open."

She'd already told Joanna, during one of their frequent video calls, that she'd met someone. She hadn't meant to, but they'd always been close and the news had just slipped out.

She'd been careful not to say too much, though. She hadn't wanted her sister to worry about this whirlwind romance, not when she was so far away.

*　　*　　*　　*

Joanna had been travelling for more than an entire day and she wished her plane would hurry up and land. This last lap of the journey seemed to be taking for ever.

Her decision wouldn't seem real until she'd shared the news with Victoria. And, not knowing how her sister would react to the plans, she wanted to get the revelation over and done with as soon as possible. It was important that they should start the New Year on the right foot.

Victoria seemed to have met some man while Joanna had been away, though. She had been positively cagey when they'd spoken. Joanna frowned as she wondered if there might be more to this romance than her sister had admitted to.

"It'll be all right, you know," the woman sitting beside her told her reassuringly. "You're safer in a plane than you are in a car, they say."

Joanna smiled to acknowledge the woman's concern. She'd obviously mistaken her nervous fidgeting for fear of flying.

"Were you on holiday in New Zealand?"

The woman seemed intent on making conversation. At first Joanna suspected she was trying to distract her from her supposed fear. But then she noticed the tremble in her hands and realised that this stranger was the one who needed the distraction.

"Not exactly," she said, happy to oblige. Chatting would make the time pass faster, after all, and doing a good turn was a bonus.

"I was made redundant when the business I worked for closed down," she confided. "So I took the opportunity to go to visit my son and his family. I've been staying with them for the past three months."

"How lovely."

Joanna smiled. It *had* been lovely – and she was already missing them dreadfully even though it wasn't long since she'd said goodbye.

It turned out the woman was making the mirror of Joanna's journey, and was planning to spend New Year's Eve and the whole of January with her daughter and family in Scotland.

Before Joanna knew it the plane was landing – and she and Elise were the best of friends. It turned out she lived fairly close to Joanna's family in New Zealand, too.

"Keep in touch," Elise said as they went their separate ways.

With phone numbers exchanged and contacts already forged on social media sites, there would be no excuses, and Joanna was very much looking forward to following up on the chance meeting.

But first she had to get over the hurdle of the next few hours.

The sisters had always been close and this was going to mean a big change to their lives.

* * * *

Victoria had been waiting by the window for the past hour. It was already after seven and the house was ready, food laid out, bubbly in the fridge. All she needed was her guests to arrive.

She heard the car before she saw it, accelerating up the hill towards the house. When it stopped outside she rushed out into the dark, drawing her cardigan closer about her to ward off the chill.

"You look fantastic," she told Joanna, taking in her new blonde highlights and fashionable coat.

"I thought it was time I started making a bit of an effort," she said. "I know I let myself go after the divorce and then losing my job."

Victoria hugged her tight. It had been a difficult time and she was pleased Joanna seemed to be starting to recover her confidence.

"Come in out of the cold," she said, leading the way inside.

"That's a lot of food." Joanna glanced at the buffet Victoria had prepared.

"It's only a few nibbles." Victoria mentally kicked herself as she realised she'd missed the ideal opening to share the news that they wouldn't be alone this Hogmanay.

Maybe she should wait until Harry actually arrived, though. It might be a bit unfair to spring him on Joanna unannounced, but if he was here it would be easier to explain why it was so important that he join them.

She glanced at the clock on the mantelpiece. It was already gone eight. He would be here soon enough.

A warm fire blazed in the hearth and the lights from the Christmas tree flickered brightly, adding to the cosy, festive feel as they sat down and began to chat.

"So," Victoria began, "tell me about your time away."

Joanna laughed.

"I've already told you most of it. I've got more photos on my phone, if you want to have a look. The wee ones have really grown – and I miss them all so much already."

The photos were mainly of Victoria's nephew and his wife and children, punctuated by the odd scenic memento of days out.

But, despite the fact there were no photographic clues, she knew her sister well enough to get the feeling Joanna was keeping something from her.

She was about to ask when Joanna turned the tables.

"Now then," she said, sitting back and looking thoughtfully at Victoria. "Do you want to tell me why you've put out so much food for just the two of us?

"And why do you keep looking at the clock? Are we expecting anyone else – maybe this man you mentioned in passing? Harry, wasn't it?"

Victoria smiled as she realised she'd been rumbled.

*　　*　　*　　*

Joanna wondered if she should be offended that Victoria hadn't bothered mentioning that Harry would be joining them. Then she decided against it as she realised she was keeping a secret, too.

"The relationship sounds serious," she said and was surprised when Victoria blushed. "So, you've been seeing each other since I went away?"

"Pretty much." Victoria took a sip of her drink.

"You never did get around to telling me how you met."

"At work. He's a new client and my colleague who he was supposed to be meeting had taken ill, so I stepped in to take him to lunch." Victoria smiled. "And when lunch was over, he asked if I was free for dinner that night."

Joanna didn't want to be negative about the situation when Victoria was obviously so happy, but she only hoped her sister wasn't heading for a disappointment.

"It all seems a bit rushed, if you don't mind me saying."

"There's no point in hanging around when you get to our age."

Now was the moment for Joanna to reveal her plans. She took a deep breath.

"You're not the only one facing new adventures," she said. "I have something to tell you, too."

*　　*　　*　　*

Joanna and Harry hit it off immediately, just as Victoria had known they would. However, she couldn't shake off the sense of unreality that, after more than 50 years, this was the last Hogmanay she would spend with her sister.

"I'm so looking forward to starting a new life in New Zealand," Joanna said as they waited for midnight, drinks at the ready. "I'll miss you, of course – and all my friends. But I met so many lovely people when I was over there. In fact, I even made a friend on the plane coming home."

Despite the shock, Victoria was gladdened to see the old spark of adventure in her sister's eyes again.

"I'm going to miss you so much," she said. "Next Hogmanay won't be the same without you here."

"We can video chat at midnight," Joanna suggested.

"Your midnight or mine?"

"Both."

They laughed.

"I have a better idea," Harry broke in, putting his arm round Victoria's shoulders. "Why don't we spend next Hogmanay in New Zealand? We could kill two birds and make it our honeymoon."

Victoria laughed at her sister's stunned expression.

"That's my big news," she revealed, grinning. "It's why Harry came round tonight – so you could meet him and we could tell you together that we're getting married. Though you stole our thunder somewhat with the news that you're emigrating."

Joanna's silence lasted only a few moments. Soon she was on her feet and hugging Victoria and Harry in turn – just as the bells rang out.

"Happy New Year," Joanna cried, before hugging them both again.

If anyone had told Victoria even a few months ago that their worlds would soon be so changed, she wouldn't have believed it. Both she and Joanna had been expecting to settle into comfortable middle age.

Instead, they were both starting out on new adventures.

Whoever would have thought it?

"Happy New Year," she replied. ■

Making Music

by Cilla Moss

THE song that came on the car radio was a 70s classic – Nick's era – and he hummed along as he pondered 7 Down on his crossword under the light of a streetlamp.

It was a miserable, rainy night, but he was cosy enough inside his taxi and didn't mind the weather.

This was the spot where he always waited for Marie: across the road from the train station. And Marie was always late. So when the passenger door opened he was caught by surprise – until he saw that it wasn't her.

"Henderson Close, please," the young woman said, climbing inside and hauling a music case into the foot well at the same time.

"Very sorry, love, but I'm not available at the moment," Nick said.

"Oh." She saw that his *For Hire* sign wasn't lit, and blushed. "Sorry."

"Have you got a mobile? Give the office a ring and ask them to send a cab out. You can stop here in the dry while you wait. What do you play?"

"Clarinet," she said, lifting the case by the handle proudly as if to show it off. "I've just been to an audition, actually."

"How did it go?"

She grimaced.

"Not sure. I was pretty nervous. I might have messed it up. Oh, well," she said with false brightness, "there's always catering college."

"I'm sure you did better than you think."

They usually do, he thought, remembering Marie.

*　　*　　*　　*

The first time he'd met Marie she was on her way to her first music exam, and had booked a taxi to take her to the station. Marie, at forty years old, had decided to take up the cello. She was as nervous as a ten-year-old.

She stuck in Nick's memory not because of the massive cello or her wide brown eyes, but because he happened to be the one to pick her up after her exam, too, and the contrast was remarkable.

On the way to her exam she'd been almost silent, and slightly green. Afterwards, she was so delighted that she chatted all the way home.

She told him all about her lifelong dream of learning the cello, and how she'd been paying for her daughter to have lessons, but her daughter was so unenthusiastic that Marie took them over. Now was her time, she decided.

A year later, when it was time for her next exam, she requested Nick to take her to the station again, determined to do everything just as she had the year before.

By the time of her third exam, Nick thought of them as friends. She called him her good luck charm.

Unfortunately, it didn't last. Marie's fourth exam was a disaster.

"It's just been such a horrible year," she confessed to him when he took her, not home, but to a quiet café where he dosed her with tea and fudge brownies. "Practice hasn't really been a priority . . ."

Illustration by iStock.

She was in the middle of a divorce, she told him. No-one to blame; just horribly sad.

Nick could only pat her hand and offer her tissues. He'd never been married, but he did know what a broken heart felt like.

He expected that to be the last time he saw her. So he was delighted when, three months later, he was sent by the dispatch office to her address.

When he arrived at Marie's house she was sitting on the wall outside, one arm around her cello.

"Retakes," she said with a grin.

This time, when he picked her up from the station two hours later, she was wearing a huge smile. The exam had obviously gone well.

Nick greeted her with a bunch of tulips.

"What's this?" she said, flushing. "I don't even know if I've passed yet."

"These aren't for passing. They're for not giving up."

She was flustered; he was flustered; there was so much shyness in the car that they made it all the way to her house in silence.

Suddenly she said, "Would you like to hear me play something?"

It was a warm, sunny afternoon. Marie unzipped her cello case and sat on the low wall of her front garden, settling herself behind the cello.

Nick leaned against the hood of the taxi and watched, rapt.

It wasn't the most slick or skilful playing. The piece was short, and quite simple; once or twice she stumbled. But Nick thought it was the most moving piece of music he'd ever heard. He'd never before had a concert played just for him. The sunshine, the resonant notes, the vision of Marie straight-backed and absorbed in playing – it was all too lovely.

He waited as she packed the cello away, and then he said simply, "Thank you." He noticed that she took as much care with the flowers as she did with her cello.

"This was so kind of you, Nick," she said. "I can't tell you how nice it is to have some encouragement. See you next year?"

*   *   *   *

So every year at around this time he was parked in the same spot, waiting for Marie, no matter how long she took.

"There she is now," he said, sitting up with a smile as he saw Marie coming out of the station, pulling her cello on a luggage trolley.

He and the girl had been chatting for a while now, and he'd told her all about Marie; he was happy for any excuse to talk about her.

"Has she been to another exam?" the girl asked.

"That was last week – she's halfway through a diploma now," Nick said proudly. "But today she's been to a final rehearsal with her community orchestra." He opened his car door. "I'll go and give her a hand."

"I'll be going, too," the girl said, picking up her clarinet. "My taxi will be here any minute. Thanks for letting me sit out of the rain."

"Any time," Nick said, shaking her hand. "I hope you get good news. Either way, you stick with the music. You never know where it might lead."

"Who was that?" Maria asked as Nick joined her.

"Fellow musician," Nick said. "I've got a soft spot for them." He pulled Marie to him for a kiss. "Hello, love. How did it go?"

"It was wonderful," she said brightly. "If I didn't feel so sick with nerves about Saturday I'd be really looking forward to it." She put her arm around his waist. "You're definitely coming, aren't you?"

"Wouldn't miss it for the world."

"I thought you might be sick of my playing by now."

Hearing Marie play the cello every night, in the house that they'd bought together after they were married, was one of Nick's greatest joys. He wouldn't swap it for anything.

"I'll cope," he said.

She pinched his arm.

"Come on, let's go. We can't just sit here and wait for the rain to stop."

He looked out at the grey sky and the soft rain; Marie on one arm, her cello in his other.

"Why not? I'm in no hurry." ■

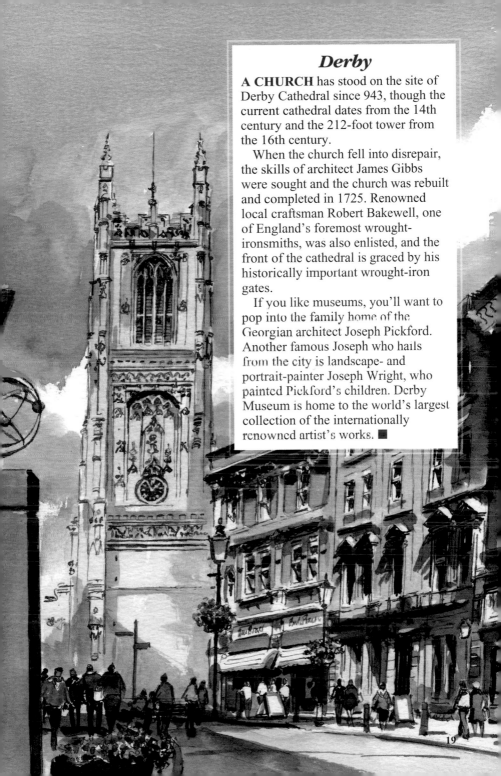

Derby

A CHURCH has stood on the site of Derby Cathedral since 943, though the current cathedral dates from the 14th century and the 212-foot tower from the 16th century.

When the church fell into disrepair, the skills of architect James Gibbs were sought and the church was rebuilt and completed in 1725. Renowned local craftsman Robert Bakewell, one of England's foremost wrought-ironsmiths, was also enlisted, and the front of the cathedral is graced by his historically important wrought-iron gates.

If you like museums, you'll want to pop into the family home of the Georgian architect Joseph Pickford. Another famous Joseph who hails from the city is landscape- and portrait-painter Joseph Wright, who painted Pickford's children. Derby Museum is home to the world's largest collection of the internationally renowned artist's works. ∎

Hearts And Paper Lace

by Pamela Kavanagh

BEFORE shutting up shop for the night, Aggie Barret inspected her cupboard to make sure she had the ingredients for her special buns. With St Valentine's Day approaching, she didn't want to run short – and you never knew when a few extra might come in useful.

No sooner had the thought entered Aggie's head than a face appeared at the hatch that comprised the shop counter.

Aggie had turned the front parlour of her small terraced home into a business after her Bob had passed on and an income was required. Baking being her strong point, she had provided the community with bread to order, and delicious pies and cakes, ever since.

"Why, Netta, lass," she said to the fresh-faced girl who stood waiting. "What can I get you? I've a nice raspberry sponge here. Or is it to be your gran's cherry scones?"

Constance Brown, a harridan if ever there was one, had a liking for cherry scones and Aggie made sure of a regular supply. Anything that helped keep the family peace was worth the effort, to her mind.

"I'll take two scones and the sponge cake, please, Aggie. It's Da's night for playing darts at the Bull tonight and Mam's turn to host the knitting group, and with it being washing day and Gran's rheumatics playing up, there's been no time to prepare any refreshments myself."

Aggie nodded understandingly. She knew how hard Netta worked in the house and thought it a shame the girl had little freedom to enjoy herself as a young person should.

But there, it was all part of life's rich tapestry, as her mam would have said. Aggie often wanted to unpick some of that tapestry and remake it with her own threads, which would have been better disposed towards girls like Netta Brown.

She slipped the raspberry sponge and scones into paper bags, noticing that the girl's usual smile was not forthcoming.

"There you are, lass. That will be one and sixpence," she said, adding

Illustration by Ruth Blair.

tentatively, "Is all well with you?"

Netta's blue-green eyes clouded.

Aggie waited. As well as providing folks with home bakes, she was known for lending a listening ear – and she prided herself on never letting a customer's woes go any further.

Behind Netta, the village street had darkened to a chilly late January dusk and William the lamplighter was doing his rounds, bringing soft pools of light along the cobbled thoroughfare.

A horse and cart rumbled noisily past, the driver casting them a curious glance over his shoulder, and Netta waited until it had gone before continuing.

"Aggie, do you believe in charms?"

"Well, there's plenty that do."

"My friends Dorrie and Pru swear by them. Last Valentine's night Dorrie put a myrtle leaf under her pillow and dreamed she saw her true love. It was Freddie Pole and now they're betrothed.

"Freddie sent her a card, all crimson hearts and lace. It wasn't signed, of course, but she knew it was from him because of the dream."

Aggie wondered where all this was heading.

"And the other lass, Pru, was it?"

Netta nodded.

"Pru said if you look into a dew pond at midnight, you see your future husband reflected there. She saw her Liam and now they're wed and Pru's expecting their first come midsummer. The thing is, I've tried both charms and nothing's happened."

"Do I take it there's a young man involved here?" Aggie had no idea how this could be. Since when did Netta have time to cast her eye over the lads hereabouts?

"Not exactly. They're mostly all spoken for, and if I don't find someone soon I'll be left on the shelf. It's not that I mind keeping house for Mam and looking after Gran –"

"But you'd rather have your own home to see after," Aggie finished for her. Netta made a wry face.

"I shouldn't grumble. There's worse things than having no sweetheart. Oh, well, I'd best get back."

She handed over her payment and disappeared into the night.

There were no more customers and as Aggie bolted the hatch, her mind was busy. Something could surely be done to ease Netta's situation. But what?

$$* \quad * \quad * \quad *$$

Jack Lowe left the village and turned the horse for the mill. It had been a long day but a lucrative one; his money pouch bulged gratifyingly, due to every single delivery of freshly milled flour being honoured by payment in full, as his business terms stipulated.

Start as you mean to go on had been Jack's maxim when he had taken over from his uncle in the new year. Jack knew how his relative had slaved, year in, year out, earning barely enough to keep body and soul together, and all because he had not been firm from the outset – no payment, no goods.

Old and world-weary, Walter Lowe had given up and gone to spend the rest of his days with his unwed sister on the coast, leaving Jack a workable mill and a decrepit mill-house that had not seen a lick of paint in decades.

The horse pricked his whiskery ears and increased his pace slightly, sensing his stall and the full manger that awaited. Jack wished the same enthusiasm could be mustered for his own supper.

He had hoped to purchase a meat pasty from the hatch-in-the-wall shop he had passed on the way in, but had got distracted. A girl had been talking to the shopkeeper, a shapely girl with a pretty face, from what he could see in the gentle light of the street lamp.

A sweetheart to woo was beyond his wildest dreams, for what lass would take on a struggling miller and a home that needed more attention than he could afford the time to give it?

The outline of the mill appeared in the chancy moonlight. Jack jigged the reins, heading the horse for his warm stall and himself to his unlit hearth and dubious meal of hard cheese and yesterday's bread.

Early next morning Jack retraced his journey to the village and halted the horse and cart outside the hatch-in-the-wall shop.

"Mistress Barret? Good morrow to you. I've called to introduce myself –
Jack Lowe from Lowe's Mill. You'll know my uncle has retired?"

The woman nodded.

"I had heard a rumour, yes. Pleased to meet you, Jack. It's a blessing to
know the mill is to continue. Goodness knows where I'd get my flour if it
closed down."

"No worries on that score, mistress. I'll be pleased to do business with you."

Jack outlined his terms of payment, softening the words with a smile that
brought endearing crinkles to the corner of his dark eyes.

"I think you will find I never was one to run up debts," Aggie assured him.

"I allow not all are tarred with the same brush. No offence meant, mistress."

"None taken, Jack. I'm all for a direct approach, myself. You know where
you stand with folk that way."

A nod enforced her statement, and reaching for a paper bag, she popped a
couple of teacakes into it from the wooden tray on the table at her elbow.

"Here, lad, a small welcome offering from me."

The teacakes were still warm from the oven and gave off an appetising
aroma, and Jack's stomach grumbled.

"Many thanks, mistress. Most grateful, I'm sure. I were about to enquire if
you had a loaf to spare but this is better still. I polished off the last of my bread
for supper yesterday."

"And came out with no breakfast inside you? Tsk, that won't do at all! It
seems to me you need a wife to look after you, young man."

The motherly scolding brought a chuckle from Jack's throat.

"Aye, you could be right. Someone fine and bonnie, like the girl I saw here
yesterday when I were passing." What made him say that, Jack had no idea,
but no sooner were the words out than he saw the truth in them.

"I'd not stand a chance there. Girls like that are snapped up double quick.
It's the flibbertigibbets that get left, and they're not for the likes of me."

"Quite right, Jack. I'm thinking that's Netta Brown you're speaking of. No,
Netta's not wed, and no betrothal in the offing, either."

"That does surprise me. All the same, courting is far from my mind at
present, what with the business to get going and a house that inna fit to bring a
cat into, let alone a wife." Jack's cheerful face was momentarily bleak.

"I'd best be on my way. Oh, and put me on your list for a daily loaf, if it
please you, mistress. I'll likely be passing so can always call for it."

A nod of farewell, and Jack boarded the cart and sent the horse clopping
away, leaving Aggie staring after him musingly.

Now there's a young fellow worth his salt, Aggie thought, as the horse and
cart disappeared into the morning murk. Undoubtedly hard working, level
headed, steadfast. If anyone was suited to Netta Brown, it was he – and Netta
had captured his interest, Aggie could tell.

In the next breath, she sighed. With Jack's mind set on making a success of the struggling mill and Netta's home situation not the easiest, bringing these two young people together seemed an impossible task. She would just have to give the matter some thought.

*   *   *   *

Over the course of the day Aggie did just that, but nothing came to mind. She baked the extra loaf for Jack and every morning he called for it. He always spared a moment to chat and it came as no surprise to Aggie when Netta's name cropped up in the conversation.

"I saw her again yesterday," Jack said one morning at the start of February. "She gave me a smile – nothing forward, like. Just natural-seeming."

The fact that Netta was aware of the new young miller and had conveyed her interest to Aggie, she kept to herself. Actions spoke louder than words and it was action that was required here.

"Did you get to speak to Netta?" she asked Jack.

"Nah. I were in a line of traffic. Any road, what good would come of it? I've already said I'm not in a position to go courting. You've not seen the state of the mill-house."

"Tsk! Who's bothered about a bit of ramshackle? I would have settled in a tin shack with my Bob if need be."

"Really?"

"Really and truly. Next time you see Netta, stop and have a word. You could start by sending a valentine."

"I'll think about it," Jack said.

It seemed to Aggie that something, maybe a secret fear of rejection, was at the root of Jack's reticence. Help was definitely needed here.

That evening she was sitting toasting herself by the kitchen range, perusing her mam's old handwritten recipe book, when the idea struck.

Every Thursday without fail, Netta's gran went to the lending library to change her books. All Aggie had to do was keep her eyes skinned for the woman's return. The rest was up to Lady Luck.

*   *   *   *

Sure enough, at around mid-morning, she spotted Constance Brown, making a great show of leaning on her walking stick, bag of books in her free hand and wearing her habitual sour look.

Aggie, fixing a welcoming expression on her own good-humoured face, left the shop and went to speak to her.

"Why, Constance. What a stroke of luck. Just the person I wanted to see."

"Oh? Why's that, then?"

No word of greeting, not even a smile. Time someone took you in hand,

My Little Visitor

IN the garage, something's changed,
It's not so tidily arranged.
There's paper scattered – what a mess!
Who's been in here? Let me guess.
Nibbled boxes, bird seed spilt,
Evidence a nest was built!
It seems I have a little guest,
(Can't possibly call him a pest).
He's fast asleep and oh, so cute –
A field mouse, in my walking boot!

Emma Canning.

madam, Aggie thought.

"Constance, I'm finding myself a little pushed at the shop and could do with some temporary help." Aggie's fingers were mentally crossed. "I remembered what a marvellously light hand you always had with pastry. Could I call upon you to put in some time on St Valentine's Day? That would leave me free to deal with my special buns and the customers, you understand."

Utter horror crossed the woman's face.

"Me? Work in a bakery kitchen? I couldn't possibly. My rheumatics, you know."

Having seen how smartly Constance could step out when she thought no-one was watching, Aggie was tempted to make a brisk riposte, but bit it back. Diplomacy was called for here.

"It would be in your interest, naturally. I'd not stint on wages. Oh, I allow that the march of time does rather make itself felt, but there, if making a few pies really is beyond your capability . . ."

The black eyes flashed in rebuke.

"Did I say that? Did I? Thinking on, I daresay I could manage a day – just to help you out, of course."

"Six of the morning of the fourteenth until closing time," Aggie said, and wondered how she would ever cope with being in a confined space with this one for the entire day. Still, anything that helped pave the path of true love . . .

Constance considered the proposal, and gave a nod.

"Very well. I do confess a little money of my own would come in useful."

"There then, you can treat yourself to a smart new cane to help you along," Aggie could not help but say. "See you Monday, Constance. Six o'clock sharp."

She gave her neighbour a nod and returned to her shop, well pleased. With Netta's mam out of the house on one of her endless social rounds and Constance under Aggie's eye at the shop, the way was clear for Jack and Netta to become acquainted. Aggie only hoped that Cupid was hovering, bow and arrow at the ready.

✳　✳　✳　✳

The morning of the 14th began in an orderly enough way, with Constance making custard tarts and fruit pies at one end of the kitchen table and Aggie pounding the dough for the Valentine Specials at the other.

Presently the mouth-watering smell of baking spiced with cinnamon drifted, and Jack remarked upon it when he stopped by for his bread.

"By, something smells good, Aggie."

"That will be my special buns for the day." Aggie lowered her voice. "Did you go ahead with the card for you-know-who?"

"No. I had a look at what was on offer but there was nothing I wanted to send. All that paper lace and stuff seemed a tad overdone to me."

"Oh. Never mind. Thinking on, could you do me a favour, Jack? Drop this order off at Netta's for me. Twenty-two Moorland Street. You'll find her at home. Should you call mid-morning the kettle will likely be on."

"And Netta's folks?"

"That's all in hand. Here, I'll put in a couple extra for you both. Now get moving, lad, before that horse takes root on the road."

Aggie thrust the bag of Specials at him and silently wished him luck.

✳　✳　✳　✳

St Valentine's Day that year turned out as hectic as ever, though not as wearing as Aggie had supposed. Constance Brown actually enjoyed her sojourn as second cook and offered her services again, should they be required.

She wasn't such a bad old stick, really, Aggie thought. She just needed a purpose in life, and as winter lost its grip and spring sailed in on green wings, the two women became friends.

As for Netta and Jack, their courtship went from strength to strength. Nobody could take an aversion to the hard-working young miller and Netta's family was no exception. Come harvest time, Aggie was overjoyed to receive a request for a wedding cake.

Which just went to show that paper lace and hearts were fine for some, but for others it was her Valentine Specials that did the trick. ■

Illustration by Ruth Blair.

Forty Acts Of Kindness

by Ann Hilton

AROL cracked an egg into a bowl, added half a pint of water and beat them together. She snipped the corner off the packet and tipped batter mix into a second bowl. Gradually she added the liquid to the dry mixture and then whisked vigorously until it was smooth.

She'd cooked a lot when her son Mark was small, cakes, biscuits and jams, and she'd have made her pancakes from scratch with fresh milk. But now, just for herself, she couldn't be bothered.

It was only because she loved pancakes so much that she was making them at all.

Once they had cooked, Carol sprinkled her pancakes with sugar and squeezed on some lemon juice. The smell made her mouth water. Then she carried the plate into the lounge, sank wearily on to the sofa and flicked on the television with the remote.

Carol watched as a group of women dressed in aprons raced with their frying-pans, tossing yellow pancakes as they went.

"Tradition has it that a housewife from Olney heard the shriving bell while cooking pancakes and ran to the church in her apron still carrying her frying-pan," the presenter explained.

"Modern-day housewives must toss their pancakes at least three times as they race to serve them to the bell-ringer and receive a kiss in return."

A beaming Mrs Aston was pictured with a bearded bell-ringer and was proclaimed the winner.

"Of course, Pancake Day, or Shrove Tuesday, was traditionally a time for eating up all the rich food in the house in preparation for Lent, a time of fasting for forty days before Easter," the presenter continued.

He began asking local people if they planned to give anything up for Lent. A few gave predictable answers, saying they were abstaining from chocolate, smoking or alcohol.

As a teenager, Carol had given up chips one year, not through any religious motivation, but as a way of losing weight. And she had done. But she'd put it all back on eating chocolate at Easter.

Another year she'd given up sugar in tea and coffee and she'd never needed to sweeten hot drinks since.

Carol turned the TV off. She felt that over the years she'd given enough things up to last a lifetime, and none of them anything to do with Lent.

At eighteen she'd passed up a place at university to study English Literature to stay near a boyfriend who didn't want her to leave. Instead she'd settled for a place at the local college where she trained to be a hairdresser.

Two years later they'd broken up, but by then Carol had a job in a good salon and was enjoying having money to spend and friends to go out with. But part of her had always regretted not doing a degree.

Some years later she'd married Edward. She'd had to give up her job when he was relocated to the West Country. She'd got work in another salon but she missed her friends.

When Mark was born two years later she'd gone part time. She'd wanted more children, but after two miscarriages and an ectopic pregnancy she'd resigned herself to letting that dream go.

Mark was a bright boy who enjoyed sport and was good at it. Carol and Edward were out in sun, wind and rain cheering him on in football matches; they were there on the sidelines at athletics meetings and clapping his achievements from the poolside in swimming competitions.

He brought them a lot of joy. But the years had flown and as a young man Mark had developed a love of travelling. On one of his adventures he'd met Lizzie, an Australian, and fallen in love.

Carol had been delighted when they married, but somehow she'd thought they would live in the UK, not emigrate to Australia. It had been hard to let Mark go.

＊　　＊　　＊　　＊

Carol picked up the photo of Edward from the sideboard. His smile lit up his face and his eyes had that mischievous twinkle she remembered so well. The illness had struck suddenly, without warning, and he'd been gone within a year.

Carol fumbled for a tissue in her sleeve and blew her nose.

Once Mark and Lizzie had gone back to Australia after the funeral, Carol had withdrawn into her shell.

She was aware that people didn't know what to say to her, and rather than see their embarrassment she'd chosen to keep her own company, refuse social engagements and keep herself to herself.

She'd given up her hairdressing job to nurse Edward and hadn't been able to face going back to such a sociable occupation.

Hairdressers had to be upbeat and positive when chatting to clients. No-one wanted a miserable, long-faced person styling their hair.

Instead, she'd found a part-time office job where she could just keep her head down, get her work done and then go home.

＊　　＊　　＊　　＊

The following morning Carol drove the short distance into town, parked the car and headed for the bank.

In the high street, a young man in a red scarf and matching bobble hat thrust a leaflet and a daffodil into her hand.

"No, thank you," Carol started to protest.

"It's just a gift," the smiling young man was saying, "to wish you a good day."

"Oh." Carol pushed the leaflet into her pocket, clutched the yellow daffodil tightly and hurried on. "Well, thanks."

The man gave her an uncomplicated smile, already looking for the next passer-by.

By the time she got home the daffodil was drooping.

"I need reviving, too," Carol thought as she popped it into a glass of water. She put the kettle on.

As she hung up her coat something in the pocket crackled. She fished out the crumpled leaflet and was about to drop it in the bin.

The heading – *40 Acts* – caught her eye.

"Don't give up – give away for Lent."

There wasn't a lot of text. Carol skimmed through it.

"Try forty acts of kindness over the forty days of Lent. What could you do for someone else?"

* * * *

That afternoon a man with a big holdall knocked on the door. He waved an ID card at Carol. She opened her mouth to send him on his way when the words of the leaflet flashed into her mind.

"Good afternoon, madam, I'm selling household goods. Can I show you? Is there anything you need? I've got clothes pegs, ironing board covers, feather dusters . . ."

"Um, I could so with some dusters," Carol heard herself saying.

The man unzipped the bulging bag and pulled out a pack of yellow dusters.

"What about oven gloves? I've got a choice of two designs." He produced a blue and white striped mitt and a red and white double glove.

"No, no oven gloves, thank you."

"I have a range of tea towels, best-quality linen," the man offered.

"Just the dusters," Carol said.

She paid the man and closed the door.

* * * *

The next morning as she got the marmalade out of the larder Carol noticed an unopened box of chocolate biscuits on the top shelf. They were left over from Christmas. She checked the sell by date – still OK.

On a whim she took them into the office.

If the other staff were surprised by this unusual gesture they didn't let on, but just thanked her. Carol felt pleased.

After work she stopped at the supermarket. As she put her coin in to release a trolley a young woman came up, rummaging in her purse.

"Bother, I'll have to go in and ask for change," the woman muttered.

Carol knew she had another £1 coin in her own purse. She thought of the leaflet.

"Here, have this one," she said.

As she pushed her own trolley into the shop Carol felt a little bubble of joy inside.

* * * *

Over the next weeks it became addictive, this desire to do a good turn. Carol found herself looking for opportunities to help others. Not big things – just small kindnesses that improved someone else's day.

She took a bag of clothes she hadn't worn for ages to the Oxfam shop; she bought a "Big Issue" from a man outside the post office, and then held the door open for a mother with a pushchair.

She complimented the receptionist at work on the green scarf she was wearing.

"It really suits you," she said. "Such a lovely colour."

In the supermarket she retrieved a packet of cornflakes from a high shelf for a lady in a wheelchair and let someone with only a few items go before her at the checkout.

It gave her a warm feeling inside.

* * * *

Carol wasn't particularly friendly with the people who lived in her close. When she arrived home from town one day she recognised the gentleman who lived on the corner coming out of the house next door. Instead of scurrying indoors Carol smiled and said hello.

"Hello," he said, "I've just been in to see Janice. She's not well. She's got flu."

"Oh, dear," Carol said, "poor Janice."

Her instinct was to stay away; she didn't want to catch the flu. But next day Carol bought some flowers and took them round to her neighbour. She could hear Janice's Jack Russell barking behind the door before it opened.

"Hello. I'm sorry to hear you're ill," Carol said. "I've brought you these." She held out the pink roses.

"Thank you," Janice said, wrapping her light blue dressing gown more tightly around herself. "Would you like to come in a moment? It's cold with the door open."

Carol stepped into the small hall and took in the cream walls and terracotta carpet. She'd never been inside before. The little dog jumped up in greeting and she bent to stroke her.

Once inside Carol wasn't sure what to do or say.

"Can I do anything for you?" she asked, thinking of the leaflet. "Make some soup or get some shopping maybe?"

The dog barked.

"Well, actually," Janice said. "I could do with some dog food for Lottie here."

On her way back with the tins Carol had another idea.

"Would you like me to take Lottie for a walk?" she offered.

* * * *

On the second day that Carol took Lottie to the park a chocolate Labrador came bounding up to them. Lottie appeared to know him. He was followed by his owner, who introduced himself as Marcus from number six.

"Where's Janice today?" he asked.

Carol explained.

"I must call round to see her."

It seemed the close was a very friendly place. Carol had been so intent on keeping herself to herself that she hadn't noticed.

*   *   *   *

Carol became more and more hooked on her acts of kindness. They made her feel good about herself – mostly. There were a few that didn't.

Like when she bought a cup of coffee for a homeless person who then complained that there was no sugar in it, and the time when she made a cake for a colleague's birthday only to find he couldn't eat it because it wasn't gluten free.

She'd also given a box of chocolates to the new girl, Sally, to welcome her to the office but then been told she was diabetic.

Still, Carol thought, sharing them round had made Sally very popular with everyone.

There had been one tricky situation when she parked next to a car with the passenger window wound down. It had been pouring with rain and Carol had thought it would be kind to try to cover the gap with a large plastic bag she found in her boot.

She'd set the alarm off and the owner had run over from the ticket machine and accused her of trying to break in!

*   *   *   *

Carol was really enjoying talking Lottie for her walks. She'd have liked a dog of her own but didn't think it was practical while she was working.

Sometimes they met Marcus and his Labrador and stopped for a chat. On one occasion Carol took a pair of rubber gloves and picked up the rubbish that had been left in the park.

A week later Janice announced, "I'm feeling much better now so I can walk Lottie myself." She saw Carol's face fall. "Of course, you could always come with us," she added.

"I'd like that," Carol said.

It became a regular thing on the days when Carol wasn't working, after they'd walked Lottie, to have coffee at one or other of their houses. Often they'd still be chatting at lunchtime. One of them would say, "I really ought to be going," and the other would suggest, "Why don't you stay for some lunch?"

*   *   *   *

Lent came to an end. Carol took the leaflet off her noticeboard and put it into the recycling box. There was more colour in her cheeks these days; she walked with a spring in her step and she'd dropped a dress size.

Her 40 small acts of kindness had changed her life. ∎

1869 Our Changing World

"The People's Friend"

FOUNDED in 1869, "The People's Friend" is the longest-running women's weekly magazine in the world. The first issue was dated January 13, 1869, and its mission statement was clear from the start.

"We intend that fully one half of the 'Friend' shall be devoted to fiction . . . the Friend being intended for fireside reading, nothing will be admitted into its columns having the slightest tendency to corrupt the morals either of old or young."

In its 150-year history, the "Friend" has had only nine editors, all of whom have remained true to those principles. Through the social upheavals, wars and natural disasters of the last 15 decades, the "Friend" has been a constant in readers' lives.

Today, the magazine is known, loved and trusted worldwide, with readers in Australia, New Zealand, South Africa and Canada as well as in the UK. It has embraced changing technology with its digital edition and a lively presence on Twitter and Facebook.

The first editor might be amazed at the changes the world has been through in the last 150 years, but we're confident he'd recognise that in moving with the times, the "Friend" remains just that – a friend for all its many readers. ■

The Dunkirk Spirit

by Richard Parsons

BETH! Beth!"

Beth Caldwell looked up, shielding her eyes against the May sun mirrored from the water of Sandcliffe harbour.

An air-defence balloon hung in the sky and there was a skein of pungent smoke from the fish-processing factory across the bay.

Rushing towards her in blue oilskins was the familiar figure of Garth Tregorran, a young trawlerman. He was tall, fair-haired and blue-eyed, with bulging muscles, the result of years spent hauling great nets.

Beth's heart began to beat harder as she saw his face etched with concern.

"What's happened?"

Rumours in Sandcliffe were rife of a German invasion; gossip from France reported they'd cut off British troops and were pinning them into a corner. The spring of 1940 might see the capitulation of the Allies just months into the conflict.

Garth stood panting.

"Your dad – he's fallen on the slipway. I'm afraid it doesn't look good."

Any thoughts of war disappeared as Beth threw down her fishing needle and the bunched net that she was mending.

A small crowd was gathered round the prostrate figure of Tom Caldwell.

"I've sent a runner for the doctor," Garth said.

Beth could see her father's leg, bent and buckled.

"Oh, Father! What have you done?"

Tom Caldwell looked up, eyes pained.

"Lass, make sure *Spirit* is all right."

Spirit Of Sandcliffe was the Caldwell family's small, battered fishing boat. Year long, every day, it chugged its way out to sea, Tom dropping nets and pots, pulling them back up, a frenzy of slippery silver or menacing pincers and claws.

"Our daily bread," her father would say.

"I've already secured her, Mr Caldwell," Garth said quickly.

Beth spoke to her stricken father as the doctor hurried up.

"I'll take *Spirit* out later and check the pots."

Illustration by Sailesh Thakrar

"Why don't I do them for you?" Garth said. "Just this once."

She turned grey eyes to him, shaking her head.

"Thank you, but you've your own to see to."

"I know, but I don't mind. If it helps you," he said, flushing slightly.

By the time the doctor had arranged for Tom to be removed to the cottage hospital, and Beth had seen him settled, it was time to retrace her footsteps to the jetty and change into her dad's old green oilskins.

A familiar sound made her glance up to see the recognisable blue and yellow boat, *Bluebell*, bobbing into harbour. She watched Garth, hand on tiller, guide the vessel into the jetty, before wrapping rope round the stanchion.

Garth had spoken to Beth about the war at its outbreak.

"I should be fighting," he said. "I mean, I'm twenty years old and fit, but the government tells me I'm in a reserved occupation. That my fishing's more important to the war effort." He'd blown out his cheeks and turned his blue eyes to her. "How can that be?"

Beth herself was just eighteen when war broke out and had hoped for a career perhaps as a teacher, or nurse.

"Something useful anyway," she said to her father. "Hands on."

Hands on, though away from boats and the sea which she loved, but in which she could see no future for herself.

Her older brother, Reg, after all, would take over the family fishing business. Now he was fighting overseas, in France.

Nets landed, Garth now approached Beth.

35

"Let me check your pots tonight," he said. "Really. It's no problem."

"There's no need, Garth. It's not like I've never done it before," she reminded him, pursing her lips.

A smattering of workers from the fish-processing factory and some construction men were waiting on the jetty. The fishermen took them across the sound, to and fro, threepence a go.

"These workers could do with a proper ferry service," Garth often commented, "now they're building that munitions factory. We've no time to fetch and carry men with our catch to land, not even at threepence a go."

* * * *

That evening, as she sat outside the small cottage where she and her father lived, needle in hand, nets bundled, Beth saw Garth once more emerging from the Lobster Pot pub. He hurried over, eyes bright. He leaned in confidentially.

"Heard the news?"

"No. What?"

"Looks like our boys are in big trouble, Beth. There's been an appeal on the news from the PM. They need boats from Channel ports to go over to France. A rescue."

"Rescue?"

"Thousands of soldiers. If we don't . . ." He pulled a face. "Well, that could be the end of it."

"When is this?" Beth asked, her mind racing to Reg in France.

"Tomorrow night," Garth said. His eyes blazed. "At last. Something that might really count. We'll be under cover of darkness and the tide's favourable. Then it'll be a case of wait and see."

"But I don't understand," Beth said. "What about the Navy?"

"The Navy ships are too big to berth, you see. We'll have to ferry our boys to and fro, or get them home."

"I'm coming, too, then. With *Spirit*."

"No!" Garth exclaimed. "It's far too dangerous."

"You mean for a girl?" Beth scowled.

They stood facing each other.

"You know I admire your determination," he said. "And you can handle a boat as well as any man, but that doesn't mean I want you to get killed."

But Beth shook her head.

"I'm coming."

Garth threw up his hands in exasperation.

* * * *

Next morning, under a benign sky, Beth took *Spirit* out once more. A few bleary-eyed workers from the factory and a couple of construction men were waiting patiently on the dockside, ready for another shift.

"Morning, miss," one said. "Any chance you could drop us off?"

She pocketed threepences and set *Spirit* chugging across the sound, a gentle breeze ruffling the water, until reaching East Sandcliffe, where she moored by the jetty. Another group of workers, finished for their shifts, waited.

"Going out or back?" one shouted to Beth.

"Out," she called, throwing a glance to open sea. "Someone'll be here soon."

That evening there was just a gentle swell in the Channel. Sandcliffe harbour was a hub of activity.

Beth had never seen so many fishing boats, schooners, smacks, a flotilla of small boats bobbing under the evening sun, riggings groaning, lanyards clinking. There were folk with vessels that Beth only saw during the summer holidays. Bankers, taxi drivers, engineers.

Each boat had no more than two men on board. Nets and pots lay strewn on the harbour walls. Anything that took up valuable space was jettisoned.

Beth had cleared *Spirit* of its gear, stowed life jackets into the small cabin where she would stand to pilot the boat. Cans of fuel lay stacked. Now, in her dad's oilskins, she waited for the sign that they were all to follow. Her nerves began to jangle.

Glancing along the harbour, she caught sight of Garth. He, too, was alone on his boat, coiling rope. Catching his eye, she waved, and she saw him disembark, hurrying towards her.

"Beth, you're not going on your own. I can't have it. Please," he said, "can't you take someone to help?"

"Are you?" she asked, a gleam in her eye. "More room for one more soldier."

He shook his head and threw her a slight smile.

"At least let us sail close by. Like when we were kids, racing."

Beth chuckled.

"Don't worry, I'll stick close by you." Their eyes met and her heart jumped. "Just in case."

He smiled grimly.

"And remember, no overloading. No point in rescuing them only for them to drown on the way home."

The flotilla set sail in a light breeze and darkening skies. Hundreds of twinkling red and green lights pushed through a gentle swell.

Through the darkness, ghostly boats came alongside but Beth kept her eyes on the near horizon, and on *Bluebell* away to her stern. Occasionally a great wash would hit *Spirit*, ripping at the wheel, and Beth would turn it to try to head into the waves.

Now it was fully dark, Beth could pick out the glow of fires round Dunkirk. By now boats were sailing past her, homeward bound. She swallowed hard, hoping that her brother Reg might be safe aboard one of them.

The flames of the town and attendant plumes of smoke were now clearly visible and the waters were alive with ghostly figures and boats.

Then the sky burst into a shower of parachute flares, like a set of small moons, and Beth could clearly make out the beach, black with men, crammed. She took a deep breath.

Coming towards her, arms raised above heads, neck deep in water, were line upon line of men, wading out. Great columns of them edged into the water as far as the eye could see, ant-like, ordered, as bombs and flares spluttered round about, ankle deep, knee deep, chest deep.

The noise of shelling was deafening. An aircraft screamed overhead, and they heard the distinct whistle of bombs.

To starboard she watched Garth hauling a shape from the sea. Then she felt *Spirit* suddenly lurch, and saw a hand grabbing to the port side.

"Wait!" Beth shouted and hurried over, heart racing. "You'll have us over."

She took in the young man's weary, frightened eyes, and those of others fast behind.

"Eight men each side, then pull yourselves on together."

"Thank you, miss, thank you. God bless you, miss," the young man said. He turned to another soldier. "Sixteen, sir."

Beth had no time to be frightened. She steadied *Spirit* as the men hauled themselves aboard. She shouted to the officer.

"I can take more!"

There were more shouted instructions, until out of the dark, two men carrying a stretcher above their heads appeared and Beth watched, heart thudding, as a figure, swathed in bandages, was stretchered on to the boat.

The figure groaned loudly as he was passed over the heads of men, and laid in the cabin.

The young officer shouted to Beth.

"They're ferrying to the destroyers, but you're best off home. Good luck."

An aircraft whined overhead and sprays of tracers shot towards a destroyer in the distance. With a stab of conscience, Beth turned *Spirit* into the wind.

The young man on the stretcher was close by, his face at Beth's shoulder. It was covered in blood-stained bandages. Beth's heart went out to him. She must get him home!

"Where are we going?" His voice took her by surprise. It was hoarse, barely more than a whisper.

"Home," she said. "England."

*　*　*　*

Gradually the lights and bangs of France subsided until *Spirit* was heading into calmer seas. The water was a passageway for boats, to-ing and fro-ing.

Faint twinklings in the distance steadily grew brighter, and Beth steered a familiar course into Sandcliffe sound.

As she moored in the harbour she could clearly see queues of soldiers. Some sat smoking or lying near the quays where scores of boats were discharging their loads.

The young man on the stretcher was lifted off.

"Here." He handed her something with a shaking hand. "What's your name?"

"Beth," she said.

"God bless you, Beth," he rasped.

As *Spirit* emptied, Beth considered her next move. Should she return? Could she? She knew what Garth would say. And her father.

She'd survived one trip. Was it too much to expect to survive another? But Garth was still there.

An Army officer hurrying up interrupted her thoughts.

"Are you going back?" he enquired. Then, looking again at Beth, he seemed taken aback. "Oh, I beg your pardon, missy. Who's the skipper here?"

"I am," Beth said, thrusting the soldier's gift into her pocket, and lifting her chin. "And yes. I am going back."

*   *   *   *

Fighting sleep, a picture of the young wounded man and the Dunkirk lines spread over the dunes and into the sea etched in her mind, she ploughed back through the waters.

She tried not to despair of her brother, or of Garth, ferrying to the destroyers under fire.

She fiddled with what was in her pocket, like a lucky charm, hoping that if she kept going, maybe, somehow, they would get out of France alive.

Dunkirk was now bathed in daylight, Beth's nerves jangling from shells landing left and right as she edged closer to the beach. A destroyer lay beached, burning.

The flames and palls of thick grey smoke were rising high in the sky, and there were still thousands of men, wading and waiting. A tide of humanity wearily edging towards safety.

"I can take twenty!" Beth shouted above the din of aircraft and battery fire as *Spirit* grounded. "Sixteen at first, then I'll have to find deeper water."

A column of soldiers was already pawing at the boat, making it lurch.

Gradually *Spirit* floated away and Beth waited while the men dragged themselves aboard. The boat swayed back and forth, dangerously low in the water.

In the distance she could see two destroyers, a fleet of boats going backwards and forwards.

All of a sudden, machine guns stuttered somewhere from up above the town. The water round about flicked with bullets.

"Home, miss!" the officer shouted just as a huge flash and explosion rent the air close by.

Eyes drawn like a magnet, Beth saw a boat disintegrate, showers and shoots of flame ripping through it, brightly illuminating its familiar blue and yellow paintwork.

Beth's heart lurched. She turned *Spirit* to starboard and headed off into the waters, mouth dry, heart hammering, dark thoughts racing in her head.

The sea was a mass of debris. A shower of sparks still rained down as *Spirit* ploughed through the swell. Hopes fast fading, Beth scanned the sea, frantic.

And then, just as she despaired, she caught sight of something bobbing in the water. Someone swimming.

Heart thudding, hopes surging, Beth drew *Spirit* close by the figure.

"Here!" she shouted.

A pair of hands grasped the side of *Spirit*. A blond head popped over the side.

"If you've too many on board, I'll swim it."

"Garth!" Beth croaked. "Thank goodness!"

The soldiers already on board, packed like sardines, began to shuffle positions. Garth was pulled into the boat, which yawed dangerously.

"How many are we?"

"Twenty-one," Beth told him.

"Come on, *Spirit*," he gasped out. "You can do it, old girl."

Beth got a look at Garth's face. He'd lost eyebrows and hair.

His face was blackened and singed; he had a lump on the side of his head oozing red, and his clothes were ripped. A gash in his hand dripped blood.

"Bring him into the cabin," Beth said to a man close by. She swallowed some water, her throat now sore. "And is there a spare blanket?"

"Lucky I was the only one on board," Garth said as he was shuffled into the cabin. "Caught me broadsides and the blast threw me into the drink."

He screwed his face, a hand reaching up to touch his head, feeling round his features.

"Can't see very well at all, actually."

"We'll get you home," Beth said. "Me and *Spirit*. You rest."

Garth chuckled, pulling a blanket round his shoulders.

"Ever the bossy one, Bethany Caldwell. I know better than to argue with you."

✳ ✳ ✳ ✳

A week later, the cottage hospital was a buzz of hushed conversations. The wards were packed, the staff run off their feet.

At the end of the room were two beds set close by each other. In one lay Tom, plaster cast leg held up on a pulley, and in another, Garth.

His head was swathed in a bandage, and over one eye was a patch. His face lit up as Beth sat down between the two of them.

"How are my pots?"

"Well!" She laughed. "There's a nice welcome. You two lounging about in bed and me doing all the work."

"You don't sound so croaky now," Tom said. "How's *Spirit*?"

"Fine. Found a few more bullet holes." She turned to Garth. "And all your pots are safe and sound. How are you?"

"Doc says the eye will be all right eventually. No permanent damage; I just have to be patient."

Tom spoke.

"We've been having a chat, lass. There will be compensation for *Bluebell*. A new boat, perhaps." He hesitated and glanced at Garth.

"So we were considering setting up together. It's the way fishing's going. The days of the small man like me are gone. Reg can take over. What do you think?"

Beth considered. There was still no news of Reg.

"I think it's a good idea." She took a deep breath. "I've been thinking, too. What if I wanted to buy *Spirit* from you?"

"You're not thinking of trawling, surely?" Garth exclaimed.

"No. But I wanted to ask you both something." She turned to face Garth. "How do you think the men would feel if I set up a proper ferry between West and East Sandcliffe?"

Garth wrinkled his nose.

"They'd be delighted. Every man round here has nothing but respect for you, even before that Dunkirk business." He looked at her seriously. "Every man."

Beth felt herself colour under his gaze, then turned to her father.

"Would you mind?"

"Mind? No-one knows boats better. It's a good idea with more factories going up, and *Spirit* will keep going for ever." He chuckled, then sighed. "I just hope we can all still earn a living after it's over."

"Did you hear Mr Churchill on the radio?" Garth asked, his face suddenly animated. "'Defend our island whatever the cost,' he said. 'We shall never surrender'."

"I did," Beth said. "And we won't."

She broke into a smile, and reached into her bag and drew out a bar of chocolate.

"I got this from one of the soldiers. As a thank you." She broke off three pieces and handed some to Garth and her father, raising her own piece in a toast. "To victory!" ■

Pitlochry, Perthshire

PITLOCHRY, situated in Highland Perthshire, is surrounded by mountains including the most striking – Ben Vrackie. Shops flank either side of the main street, Atholl Road, where there also stands a Celtic cross war memorial to the fallen. Adjacent to the cross you'll find a memorial garden offering a place for quiet contemplation.

Pitlochry fish ladder next to the power station on the River Tummel is worth a visit, where you can see the salmon making their way upstream, and the Pitlochry Dam Visitor Centre is full of information.

Aside from hillwalking and shopping, you can also visit Pitlochry Festival Theatre, which attracts in excess of 100,000 visitors from throughout the UK and abroad each year. ■

Illustration by Sarah Holliday.

The More, The Merrier

by Jan Snook

I T'S supposed to be, I don't know, a time for people to show their mothers they appreciate them, for goodness' sake!" Martha burst out suddenly, continuing a conversation – more of a tirade really, her husband Andrew thought, but had the sense not to say – that had been going on for most of the morning. "And every year it just seems to get worse!" She shook her head.

Andrew opened his mouth to speak, but Martha hadn't finished.

"It's like walking on eggshells, trying to please everybody! I mean, I really must visit my mother – after all, she's over ninety – but if we do that your mother will feel neglected, and they live too far apart for us to do both.

"Then there's Alice and Harriet: they've both said they'd like to come here, and I want to see them, of course, and the grandchildren. Harriet said little

43

Florence had been secretly making a giant card for her. But then their mothers-in-law would be offended."

Andrew opened his mouth again, but the flow hadn't stopped.

"And anyway, Alice may not really have the energy to go anywhere with a new baby. Elsa will only be seven weeks old by then.

"Alice might just be being polite, saying she'd like to come here – maybe what she really wants is to spend her first Mother's Day quietly with just the three of them."

Andrew gave a deep sigh.

"And it's even more important that we see Katie, because otherwise I'll look like the wicked stepmother!"

"Now you're really being ridiculous," Andrew said mildly, as his wife finally drew breath. "You're the only mother Katie's ever known. Goodness, I don't know what I would have done with Katie after Liz died if I hadn't met you."

Martha looked at him sadly.

"And it was all a long time ago," he added, putting an arm round her. "Katie's over forty. She's not going to suddenly cast you as a wicked stepmother."

"Well, even so. And then there's the question of Boo," Martha said, a bit defensively, running out of steam at last.

Andrew closed his eyes briefly.

"I cannot believe that I have to take the cat into consideration when making Mother's Day arrangements," he said.

"But her kittens are due right about then – we won't just be able to abandon her," Martha said in surprise.

"So whoever we do see will have to come here. Which means we still have to choose . . . Oh, it's all such a mess," she finished, her shoulders slumping.

Andrew gazed at his wife, nonplussed. How could she have blown this up into such a major problem? Whatever he said now would probably be wrong. Much safer to say nothing.

He reached out and gave her a hug instead, wondering what on earth made women get so upset about something so simple.

"I'll sort it," he said. "It's Mother's Day, after all, it shouldn't be your job to worry about it. Just buy your own mother a card, and I will do everything else."

"But . . ."

"No buts. Consider it done."

*   *   *   *

"I told your mother I'd sort it," Andrew said miserably to Harriet when she phoned later that week. "And I will, of course," he added firmly. "I've been making a list while your mother's out at her book club."

"Actually," Harriet said apologetically, "I was ringing to talk to Mum about Mother's Day. I know how much she would like us to come to yours, and Florence is dying to come, but . . .

"Oh, here's Florence now, come to say hello. I'll just put you on speakerphone."

After many shouted greetings from five-year-old Florence, Harriet continued.

"As I was saying, we'd love to come to you, but . . ."

"I do understand, you've really got to go to David's parents this year," Andrew said, hoping she couldn't hear the relief in his voice. Having three fewer people would make things easier.

"Well, actually, I was going to ask if we could bring David's parents with us," Harriet said tentatively. "They'd love to see you, and what with David being an only child – would that be OK, do you think?"

"Marvellous!" Andrew said, pulling an unseen face of horror. "The more the merrier!"

"What does that mean?" a little voice asked in the background.

"It means the more people there are, the jollier the party will be," Harriet explained, and David could hear his daughter smiling.

*　　*　　*　　*

"Oh, Alice," he said a few minutes later. "I hope this isn't an inconvenient time?"

"I don't know that there's such a thing as a good time with a new baby," Alice said, sounding tired. "But I'm sure she can wait a few minutes longer for her feed.

"Why didn't anyone tell me how tiring it would be? Or rather, why didn't I believe them?"

"Oh, sweetheart, I'm sorry. Is there anything I can do?"

"Get my mother-in-law off my back? No, that isn't fair of me, she only wants to help.

"But now she wants to come here for Mother's Day, and I really don't know how I'll cope. All I want to do is come to you that day . . ."

"Well, why don't you do that, and bring Matt's parents with you?"

What? Had those words really just come out of his mouth? Andrew felt like banging his head against the wall. He was losing it, he really was.

"Oh, Dad," Alice was saying, sounding thrilled, "that is so kind of you. Are you sure? It would make my life so much easier. And I wouldn't have to feel guilty about one of you spending Mother's Day with Elsa and not the other. Oh, Dad, you're a star!"

And, polishing his halo, Andrew went back to his list. There was no doubt about it, the numbers were getting out of hand. Where was everyone going to sit? Why had he said lunch, rather than just tea?

Boo came into the sitting-room at that point, walking rather gingerly, and looking tired and anxious.

"You and me both," Andrew said aloud. "You know, it would be really helpful if you didn't have these kittens of yours on Sunday. There's going to be quite enough going on.

"And on that subject, I did warn you about the Smiths' tomcat, if you recall. You wait – parenthood is fraught with problems."

Boo took no notice but poked her head under the sofa, then withdrew it again.

"And you certainly can't give birth in here," Andrew said, "so don't even think about it." He picked her up and carried her into the kitchen. "Look, you haven't touched your food."

Boo looked at it, but opted for her basket instead.

"Good idea," Andrew said, then headed back to the phone. He'd better ring Katie. Perhaps she had already made plans for Mother's Day, he thought hopefully.

But, of course, she hadn't. All five of them would, she assured him, be delighted to come.

"The other two are bringing their parents-in-law," he said faintly, but to his relief Katie just laughed.

"Don't worry, mine are going to Oliver's sister."

"Thank the Lord!" Andrew said, and found himself telling Katie all about the growing guest list.

"So you're up to . . . what? You, Mum, five of us, Alice plus four, Harriet plus four, Granny, Grandma and Grandpa – that's twenty! For lunch in your house! How on earth are you going to manage? And what about the food?"

"Well . . ." Andrew began, trying not to sound desperate.

"You know what? I think I'd better organise the buffet. You can be in charge of drink," she added as he started to object.

*   *   *   *

Mother's Day dawned cloudless and mild, and Andrew heaved a sigh of relief. The weatherman had promised the first proper spring day, and it looked as if he was right.

The garden was sunshine yellow with daffodils, and there were clumps of purple and white crocuses under the pear tree. Katie had arrived early to help, and the table was soon piled high with plates and glasses and cutlery and napkins.

"People were only too happy to bring something," she assured her father, as she put her own contribution, a beautifully iced cake, on the sideboard.

Fair Exchange?

I KNOW it's stolen property;
I ought to be ashamed.
The sight of gold just lured me on –
I really can't be blamed!
So though I'm very sorry, bees,
To plunder from your hive,
Your honey I just can't resist,
However hard I strive.
So could we make a bargain, bees?
To save me from your glowers,
If I may share your honeycombs,
Then you may share my flowers!

Maggie Ingall.

"But Alice has a new baby . . ."

"And a husband," Katie reminded him, smiling. "We're not still in the Dark Ages, Dad. Men can cook, too! And the mothers-in-law are both doing their bit."

* * * *

It wasn't long before the guests began to arrive, all bustling about with dishes and wishing one another a happy Mother's Day.

"I've made a jelly," Florence said proudly, tugging at Andrew's hand so that the jelly wobbled dangerously.

"And what about all the cards you've been making?" her mother Harriet asked, smiling. "Did you bring those with you?"

She winked at her father.

"I received a beautiful card this morning, but I've been conscious of other top-secret card-making going on behind my back!"

Florence gazed at her mother in astonishment.

"I haven't been making cards," she said. "I've been making invitations. Because of what Grandpa said."

"What . . .?" But Florence had run off, searching for Boo.

The doorbell rang, and the noise levels rose as the sitting-room, dining-room, kitchen and even the hall filled up with happily chatting relations.

Andrew circulated, filling up glasses, and was glad that Katie had put out a few extra plates – he'd forgotten his mother's carer would be coming, and a couple of neighbours Martha had met that morning at church had popped in as well.

The house was bursting at the seams.

"Are you going to say a few words, Dad?" Harriet was asking, just as the doorbell rang again. She and Andrew looked at each other.

"Surely everyone's here now, aren't they? There isn't room for even one more person!"

"That'll be my teachers," Florence said confidently. "I invited them."

"What?" Harriet asked, aghast, as Alice's husband went to get the door. "Florence, you can't just invite people without asking, you know that."

"But they haven't got anyone to go and see on Mother's Day. Their children live too far away, and you said . . ." Florence began, her face crumpling.

"It's quite all right," Andrew said quickly. "It was a very kind thought, Florence."

"And you said," the child continued, determined to vindicate herself, "you said . . ."

"Dad," Katie said, coming up at that moment, "I've just been into the kitchen – have you seen what's going on?" She grinned. "You'd better come. Mum's already in there. You can come, too, Florence."

They followed Katie into the kitchen, where the utility room door was standing open.

"But there are one, two, three, four, five of them!" Florence said in an awed whisper, looking at the tiny kittens. Boo was licking one of them vigorously and ignored the mesmerised audience.

"You and Katie have done brilliantly," Martha whispered in Andrew's ear. "I would have had kittens organising all of this."

"Where shall I put this?" a voice behind them said, and they all turned to greet the new arrival, who was carrying a beautiful apple flan.

"Hello, Mrs Ford!" Florence beamed at her. "Look!"

"We'd better leave Boo to it," Andrew said, smiling at Florence's teacher. "You've come just in time. Let me get you a glass."

A moment later they were all back in the sitting-room and Andrew had tapped his glass for silence.

"We're delighted to see you all, and I'm sorry it's a bit of a squash," he began. "I just wanted to say happy Mother's Day. I was just counting up, and there must be at least a dozen mothers here."

"You haven't forgotten Boo, have you?" Florence interrupted, counting on her fingers.

"As well as our cat Boo," Andrew amended, smiling at her. "which is wonderful. So let's raise our glasses: after all, as Florence has just been reminding me . . ."

"The more, the merrier!" Florence said. ■

iStock and Alamy.

The World Of Books

READERS in 1869 were treated to a feast of literature from around the world. In Russia, Leo Tolstoy finished his great work, "War And Peace". Published in book form for the first time, it would be another 20 years before an English translation appeared. It has been in print in English ever since. However, it is one of those books that people tend to know about rather than having read it in its entirety; it came top in a YouGov survey of classic novels that British people would like to read if they had the time and patience.

It is a bit of a commitment – Tolstoy's masterpiece has 559 characters and a battle scene that covers more than 20 chapters. So vivid were the descriptions of warfare that one Russian general even suggested that the novel should be required reading for Russian Army officers.

Film and television adaptations have proved popular. There were around seven million viewers for the BBC's 2016 series at its first showing.

Other works produced in the same year were "Lorna Doone", R.D. Blackmore's historical romance set in the West Country at the time of the Monmouth Rebellion in 1685, and "Good Wives", Louisa May Alcott's sequel to "Little Women". ∎

A Glimpse Of Gold

by Valerie Bowes

NOW, who can tell me what this is?"
Jo held up a picture of a purple crocus and smiled at the forest of waving hands. She scanned the eager faces, looking to see who had recognised the flower. Everybody had, it seemed. All except Katie Jones. As usual.

"It's a crocus, Miss!"

"Very good, Craig. And where will you find crocuses, Phillipa?"

"In the school garden, Miss. There's lots of them in a big circle."

"Yes," Craig said, "'cos my brother's in Mrs Cross's class, and they planted them last year."

"It's not just a circle, though, is it?"

Jo could see that most of the six-year-olds knew what she was talking about, but Katie was still the only one without a hand waving in the air.

"It's a maze," Phillipa said importantly. "To help get rid of polio."

"Do you know what polio is, Katie?" Jo asked gently, trying to get the little girl to join in with her classmates, but Katie merely shook her head. "Well, it's a very nasty disease and we plant the crocuses to raise money to help people in other parts of the world to get rid of it.

"We plant purple ones because when they get their vaccinations, they dip their fingers in purple dye to show they've had it. So get your coats on, and we'll go down and see if you can find your way through the maze and be glad we don't get polio in this country any more."

The children didn't need telling twice. It was a bright, beautiful day outside the classroom, although Jo knew they'd be glad of their coats in the chilly spring wind.

"You get white crocuses as well as purple ones, don't you, Miss?" Craig zipped up his jacket.

"And yellow ones!" Phillipa was not to be outdone.

"Yes, and they're very pretty, too." Katie had looked up suddenly with an eager look on her face that her teacher rarely saw there.

"Do you like yellow crocuses best, Katie?"

But as soon as she spoke, Katie retreated.

In the staff room later, Jo was still worrying about Katie's lack of response. Maybe it was nothing more than shyness. She and her mother had only recently moved to the district.

Coming from an inner-city school with bigger classes in which she could hide, maybe she found the amount of attention Jo could give to each child rather intimidating.

Jo made a note to ask Katie's mother at the next parents' meeting. If Katie hadn't come out of her shell by then, perhaps Megan Jones could help find a way to reach her.

The next morning, Jo asked the children to write about the Crocus Maze. She wrote the word *polio* up on the board, then let them get on with it while she pinned up pictures of spring flowers around the room.

Illustration by iStock.

The last was of a daffodil and, as she turned back to the class to see how they were getting on with their writing, she was surprised to see Katie staring at the golden flower.

Jo smiled at her.

"Pretty, isn't it, Katie? Can you tell me what it is?"

Katie shook her head. Oh, well, Jo thought, keep trying. We'll get there one day.

"But I know how it got there." Katie's voice was little more than a whisper. Jo squatted beside her chair.

"Do you? Have you planted bulbs in your garden?"

"We haven't got a garden. But I know 'cos I've seen them. They fly, and then they drop down to the earth and then the flower's there."

There was an outbreak of sniggering from the children near enough to hear. Country-bred, they all knew how daffodils grew.

"Don't be silly! You couldn't have!" Phillipa snorted. "Daffs don't fly, do they, Miss?"

Jo blinked. How could she answer this without putting Katie off? She didn't want the girl to retreat into her shell again. It might be even harder to prise her out a second time.

Katie's face began to flush.

"I did! I did! I saw it fly down our street, and then I found where it landed."

Most of the children laughed, but Craig stared at Katie with eyes as round as an owl's.

Jo got up.

"It's a lovely thought, Katie. I'd love to see a daffodil fly. Perhaps we will in a couple of weeks' time, when they all come out. Everybody look out for them, right? Now, let's see what you wrote about the crocuses. Phillipa, do you want to read yours out?"

As she went home that evening, the idea of a flying daffodil wouldn't leave Jo. On impulse, she parked her car at the end of the road where Katie lived and walked down it.

The small terrace of newly built houses was in a narrow lane with fields visible through the hedges that bordered it, still bare of leaf. Surely Katie wouldn't have wandered too far down here?

Jo turned round to begin the walk back to her car. And then she saw it. A lone daffodil, growing almost under the hedge. It was either more sheltered from the cold wind there or it caught more sun, for it was the first one she'd seen that was fully out. Most of the other green buds were still pointing skywards, the sunshine beauty furled within.

She bent down to touch the glowing trumpet. Katie had been right. She'd definitely seen a daffodil.

$*$ $*$ $*$ $*$

On the evening of the parents' meeting, Jo saw Megan Jones walking towards her across the classroom and thought she looked tired out.

"Hello! How nice to see you," Jo said as Megan took her seat opposite. "Are you settling in OK?"

Megan brushed her hair out of her eyes with a weary hand.

"Yes, thank you."

"It must be quite a change from the city," Jo persevered. "How does Katie like it?"

"Fine. I thought she'd miss the roads and shops, but she doesn't seem to."

"That's good," Jo said, a little too heartily, but she couldn't help wondering why Katie would miss roads and shops rather than her friends.

"I hope she'll soon settle into school life and start making friends with the other kids. Her school work's well up to the others, but I'm finding it hard to get her to join in with them. Have you any idea why that is? Did she have the same trouble at her last school?"

Megan dropped her gaze to her hands, which were clasped tightly together in her lap.

"She's always been a bit shy," she mumbled. "I don't think it's anything to worry about, do you?"

"Everybody copes differently and in their own way." Jo tried to be as reassuring as possible. "It's just if there's a reason why she finds it so hard to join in with all our activities . . ."

"No," Megan interrupted firmly. "There's no reason. She's still getting over the disruption of the move, I expect. So long as she's OK with her work, that's fine, isn't it?"

Jo didn't agree there, but Megan was already getting up to go and there were still other parents to see.

"Yes, I've no concerns about her progress in that quarter. Especially her writing. I always look forward to reading what she's written – like the flying daffodils! She's got a very vivid imagination."

Megan's tired face lit up in the first real smile Jo had seen from her.

"She has, hasn't she? She gets that from her dad."

Jo had the strong impression that Megan rather wished she hadn't said that, for she made a fuss of gathering her bag and saying a hasty goodbye.

But maybe it was a clue. Had Katie's parents broken up? Was it to get away from a violent husband that Megan had moved herself and her daughter to this out-of-the-way spot?

Before she had time to get her chaotic thoughts in order, Craig's dad was plonking himself in the seat Megan had just vacated with a smile as broad and cherubic as his son's and she had to stop thinking about Katie's problem.

*　　*　　*　　*

The class was busy painting daffodils. Bright yellow petals on backgrounds of even brighter green. Phillipa glanced sideways at Katie's handiwork.

"You haven't painted wings on your daffodil!" she said.

Katie reddened, but made no reply.

"But you said you saw one flying, didn't you?" Phillipa giggled.

Jo felt it was time to intervene.

"Ah, but we're painting what we can see from here and none of them have wings. Can anyone tell me what daffodils mean, when they're planted in a big square like this?"

"The Field of Hope," the class chorused.

"And what's the Field of Hope?"

"It's to help people with cancer," Craig said. "My mum wears a little brooch like a daff pinned to her coat to show she's helped."

"If crocuses help people with polio and daffodils help people with cancer, which flower helps people with CFS?" Katie flushed as the eyes of the class turned in her direction.

Jo carefully controlled her breathing and forced herself to sound matter of fact. She didn't want Katie to feel she was in a spotlight.

"What's CFS, Katie? Do you know someone who's got it?"

"It's when you're tired all the time and you have to go to a place like a hospital for tests."

She wouldn't say any more and, as it was time to clear up before the bell went for the end of the afternoon, Jo didn't push it. But she went to see Megan when she left school.

*   *   *   *

"Chronic Fatigue Syndrome," Megan said. Jo sensed a defensive shield going up. "Katie's dad has it." Tears suddenly threatened to slide down her cheeks.

"It's why we moved here. He's helping with research at the laboratories at Tuncaster, and it was too far away from where we lived before. I couldn't go and visit him." She wiped the tears away. "And because I wanted to come where no-one knew us. People don't believe it, you see. They used to call it ME and thought it was all psychological and Kevin was just being lazy. But he's not."

"If you're running up and down to Tuncaster, no wonder you're tired out with all the worry and stress," Jo said with sympathy.

"Katie misses her daddy so much." Megan sighed. "She used to be such a bright, bubbly little girl. Now she won't make any friends in case they say nasty things about him like before."

*   *   *   *

Jo had a lot to think about as the children filed in to begin the school day. But as she began to talk to them about their sums, Craig's hand waved in the air.

"Yes, Craig?"

"There's Katie's flying daffodil!"

Katie bent her head down, refusing to look at him, but Craig took her hand and gave it a little shake, pointing out of the window.

"Look, Katie!"

A bit of yellow was dancing across the playground. As they watched, it merged with the golden glow of the Field of Hope.

"It's a Yellow Brimstone," Craig told her. "It's one of the first butterflies to come out in spring, but there'll be loads later. Orange Tips and Red Admirals and Peacocks. My dad knows all about them and he lends me his books. I'll show you, if you like."

Katie nodded with a shy smile. Jo smiled, too.

"Well, when we do painting again, we'll draw lots of Brimstone butterflies."

She'd suggest sending the pictures to Katie's dad at the research labs. If fragile spring flowers could help in the fight against such diseases as polio and cancer, she didn't see why a butterfly shouldn't do the same for CFS. ∎

Swan Green, Emery Down

EMERY DOWN is a small village overlooking Swan Green and Lyndhurst in the New Forest National Park. Admiral Frederick Moore Boultbee did much to shape life in Emery Down, paying for the village church and school. The church was designed by William Butterfield, the famous Victorian architect, who also designed five almshouses endowed by Boultbee, which are still known locally as Boultbee Cottages.

Boultbee lived in the village with his niece in a thatched dwelling known as the Cottage. Not only was he a philanthropist, but during his Naval career he also co-operated in the suppression of the slave trade on the coast of Africa.

Sir Arthur Conan Doyle stayed in Emery Down for a year while researching a novel. Another famous visitor was Edward Smith, the captain of the *Titanic*. He spent his last night on dry land at Emery Down before setting off on the ill-fated ship. ∎

The Prettiest Bonnet

by Pamela Kavanagh

LOOK, Emmy! What do you think?"

Emmy looked admiringly at the hat her friend was wearing.

"It suits you. Where did you get it?" she asked.

Rose pulled the straw bonnet from her head and twirled it on her finger.

"From Fergusson's. It's plain enough now, but you wait until I've decorated it with flowers. It'll be a picture, you'll see."

Enlightenment dawned.

"Oh, you're going to enter the Easter Bonnet competition!"

"Yes, and do you know who's judging it? Matthew Conlan!"

There had been no end of gossip in the village about the Reverend Conlan's son. He had gone to war as a shy lad, prone to pimples and gangly as a bean-pole.

He had returned from the trenches four years later as a tall young soldier, handsome and confident.

"Shall you enter a bonnet?" Rose asked. "You didn't last year, or the year before that. Do, Emmy! It would be such fun!

"We could have a sort of private competition, just you and me. See which one of us Matthew likes best!"

"I might," Emmy said. "If I get time. Father's not very well, you see."

She couldn't quite restrain the sigh that came out of her mouth along with the words. Since her mother died, just before the war started, Emmy had looked after her young brothers and sisters.

And now she had her father to look after as well. When would she ever have the leisure to think about Easter bonnets?

But she found herself thinking about them more and more as the spring flowers began to show their heads. And it didn't help that Matthew Conlan seemed to be handsomer than ever as the pallor of the trenches slowly began to fade.

He'd been away, fighting in France. It gave him an added glamour that the other men in the village had never possessed. None of them, as far as she knew, had ever been further than the big town. And they'd all been too young

or too old to go to war.

Except Toby Lisson, that was. Emmy had often wondered why he hadn't been called up. He was two years older than she was. That made him seventeen when the war started, and many lads had lied about their age so they could do their bit.

Helping in his father's grocery shop was hardly an essential occupation. If the vicar's son could go, why couldn't he?

*   *   *   *

Rose was adamant that hers was going to be the best bonnet. She'd stitched a pink ribbon around the straw shell, long enough to tie in a big bow under her chin.

"I'll put violets all round the brim," she decided, showing Emmy the result. "And maybe some daffodils right in the front. What do you think?"

"I think you'll look lovely." Emmy hugged her. It would be hard not to look lovely if you had Rose's big blue eyes and her pretty hair peeping from under your hat.

"Let's see yours, then."

Emmy sighed.

"I haven't done one yet."

"But Easter's next week," Rose reminded her.

Emmy didn't need telling.

She'd collected enough onion skins to make Pace Eggs for the children.

Wrapping them around some eggs as they boiled would turn the shells a gorgeous mottled brown and then she'd rub a bit of butter on them to make them shine.

And the onions had made a thick broth for her father, to help stop the cough that plagued him.

It was better, but he still sat huddled in his old coat by the fire. It worried him that he wasn't working, but the slightest attempt to move set the cough off again.

"Don't, Father," Emmy told him. "There's time enough for you to go back to work when you're better. If you go now, you'll only be back where you started and all to do again.

"And spring's coming. You know your chest is always better when the weather warms."

"But I'm bringing nowt in, lass."

"Our Susan's helping at the dairy now. She gets her wages and Mrs Wood lets her have some butter. There's still some pennies left in the jar, and I'm doing Mrs Harding's washing tomorrow. We'll manage."

"You shouldn't be doing other folk's washing. Haven't we enough of our own?"

"Now then, Father, that's enough of that." She smiled at him to take the edge off her words. "I can do Mrs Harding's while I'm doing ours, and she'll give me some eggs and a bit of bacon off her flitch. That'll make a nice tasty supper, don't you think?"

She'd have to sides-to-middle the boys' sheets before she washed them, she thought, adding the task to her list of things to be done, otherwise Alfie or Ernest would be sure to put a foot through the thin bit and then it would be harder to mend.

The Easter bonnet would have to wait. Again.

*   *   *   *

"Come and help me look for some violets," Rose coaxed. "It's such a lovely day and a walk will do you good, Emmy."

"I've got the range to clean and the mending to do and I must get some more tea and sugar before I get the stew on, or Father will miss his brew this afternoon. And he needs some more baccy."

"I'll help you prepare the stew and then you can help me look for flowers," Rose said. "The chores can wait. And we'll call into Lisson's as we go. I'm sure Toby will drop anything you need in for you."

"You go, Emmy, my girl," her father said from his chair by the fire. "Rose is right. You ought to get out and enjoy this lovely weather while it lasts.

"Old Jim says it'll rain next week, and I've never known him wrong this thirty year."

"Oh, no, Mr Baker! Don't say that!" Rose cried. "It's the Easter Parade next week. If it rains, our bonnets will be ruined!"

"Then let's hope he's made a mistake this time, lass. Off you go now, and leave me to enjoy a pipe in peace."

Emmy allowed herself to be persuaded. Goodness knew, she needed to forget all her responsibilities for a couple of hours.

*　　*　　*　　*

The sun shone from a sky as blue as speedwell as the girls walked down the road. Emmy lifted her face to the warmth and closed her eyes for a blissful moment.

At the little shop, Rose tugged Emmy inside.

"Tell him what you need," she ordered as the young man came forward, his apron fastened to the middle button of his waistcoat and his sleeves rolled up over his brawny forearms. "You'll drop a few bits off for Emmy, won't you, Toby?"

"Of course I will. Just tell me what you want."

What did she want, Emmy wondered. To behave like the nineteen-year-old she was, instead of like the mother of four? Five, if you counted her father.

She'd been working at the stationer's in town when she left school. She'd loved it, but then Mam had died and her family came first.

Now Susan and Ernest were able to bring something in, her worries about money had lessened, but she still had them all to look after.

Sometimes she wondered if she would ever have a home and children, or whether she was destined to be just an aunt when Susan, Ernest, Alfie and little Caroline left for lives of their own. Because who would want her to be their sweetheart?

She dragged her mind away from the bleak prospect and told Toby what she required. He licked his pencil and wrote it down carefully.

"Don't you worry, I'll bring it round after I've put the shutters up this evening," he promised.

As she walked down the lane beside Rose, Emmy felt as if the weight of the world had been lifted from her, not just a few groceries. Perhaps she'd have a go at her Easter bonnet later.

She wouldn't have time to go into the town and buy a hat like Rose's, but she was sure she had an old boater on the top of her wardrobe.

A bit of new ribbon tied round it and some pretty spring flowers . . . It might not be good enough to attract Matthew Conlan's notice, but at least she wouldn't be watching the Parade from the sidelines again.

Rose grew more and more disappointed as they scoured the hedgerows.

"Where have all the violets gone?" she wailed, holding up the only two she'd been able to find. "There's usually so many of them along here, it's as if the ground's turned blue."

"Maybe it's because Easter's early this year," Emmy said. "Never mind, Rosie. There's plenty of primroses in the coppice back there. They'll look just as pretty on your hat."

"But I wanted violets!" Rose pouted. "I asked Matthew Conlan after the service on Sunday what his favourite flower is, and he said he liked violets best."

"Well, he's a poor judge if he awards the prize only to the flowers he likes," Emmy said. "He's supposed to be choosing the prettiest bonnet – even if it's covered in nettles!"

"You wouldn't put nettles on an Easter bonnet!" Rose giggled. "That wouldn't look pretty at all."

"But primroses will," Emmy reassured her.

"What are you putting on yours?"

"Oh, I haven't decided yet." She'd have to give the old hat a good clean first. Perhaps she'd do that this evening, after supper.

*   *   *   *

But when she retrieved the boater, she was dismayed to see how worn it was. There was a hole in the side.

Emmy brushed the dust off with a mounting feeling of despair, and wondered if it was even worth bothering with.

The knock at the door roused her from her dismal thoughts. Toby had brought the items she'd asked for.

He came into the kitchen to set the box on the table while she sought for her purse to pay him, and she noticed he had a slight limp.

"Have you hurt your leg, Toby?"

He reddened.

"No. It's my foot. It's all cramped up. I was born with it. That's why they wouldn't have me in the Army."

She remembered him always being a little slower than the rest of them when they were children, but she was ashamed to realise she'd never paid that much mind.

To cover her embarrassment, she rummaged in her purse for the money and counted it into his hand.

"Is that going to be your Easter bonnet?" He nodded at the hat.

"Yes," she said with a touch of defiance. "I haven't done anything with it yet, but I've got ideas."

"It'll be lovely," he said, smiling at her.

She couldn't help laughing.

"Well, it'll look better than it does now, so I hope Matthew Conlan will think so."

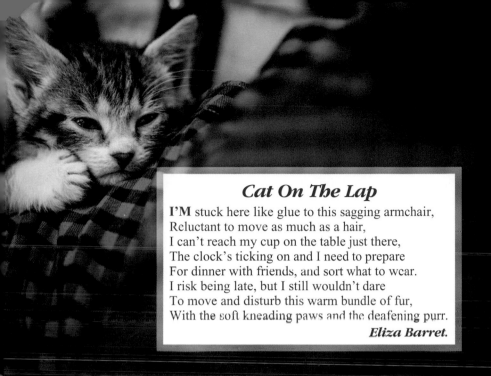

Cat On The Lap

I'M stuck here like glue to this sagging armchair,
Reluctant to move as much as a hair,
I can't reach my cup on the table just there,
The clock's ticking on and I need to prepare
For dinner with friends, and sort what to wear.
I risk being late, but I still wouldn't dare
To move and disturb this warm bundle of fur,
With the soft kneading paws and the deafening purr.

Eliza Barret.

The smile faded and she fancied he wished her good night with a shade of restraint.

*   *   *   *

The sun shone on the day of the Parade. It appeared Old Jim had, for once in his weather-forecasting career, got it wrong. The band tuned up with many an oompah, making the children giggle at the rude noises.

Boy Scouts and Girl Guides formed up in lines with the girls in their Easter Bonnets, self-conscious and blushing, behind them.

Emmy had found time to bind some blue ribbon around her boater, the ends fluttering in the unpredictable little breeze. She had hoped that some of the spring irises would be out but, like the violets, they hadn't yet bloomed.

So she fashioned a large flower out of the paper from a sugar bag, which was much the same colour, stuck it through the hole in the straw and wore the whole thing tipped rakishly over her piled hair.

Rose had threaded so many primroses through the straw of her hat that it looked as though it was made from the delicate flowers, set off by the pink bow. It was a work of art, Emmy told her, and bound to win if Matthew Conlan had eyes in his head.

He stood, flanked by his father and Mrs Pepper from the Big House, as the Parade got ready to march around the road looping the big green.

"I hope they don't take too long getting started," Rose said, looking with anxious eyes at the ominously dark cloud lining the horizon. And, as they reached the far side of the green, spots of rain began to fall.

At first, it was individual drops that made large circles on the road, but within moments, the rain was coming down in a swishing curtain. With one accord, the marchers dashed across the grass to take shelter in the church.

The vicar and Mrs Pepper had already hurried up the path and welcomed them in, but Matthew stayed in his place until the last person had joined them.

Amid laughter, the players of the tuba and the euphonium tipped water out of their instruments into the porch, and then they gathered to hear Matthew's verdict on the Easter bonnets that were drooping on their wearers' heads.

"The prettiest bonnet is . . . this one!" he said, taking Rose's hand and pulling her forward. Only one or two disconsolate maidens could be seen to disagree.

Emmy applauded as loudly as the rest and couldn't help smiling when she saw that Matthew seemed to have forgotten that he still held Rose's hand as Mrs Pepper stepped forward to present her with a small silver cup.

Ah, well. It had been nice to dream that someone might think as much of her. She pulled out the hatpins that held the boater at its jaunty angle and removed the soggy straw from her head.

Her hair was dripping down her back but she wasn't the only one to look as if she'd been pulled through a gooseberry bush backwards.

The rain eased as abruptly as it had started. Mrs Pepper called a general invitation for folk to come and partake of tea and cake at the Big House once they'd got into some dry clothes.

Emmy looked around for Rose, but she and Matthew were nowhere to be seen. She began to walk back home, thinking she'd put the hat straight on the midden.

It hadn't been much before; it certainly wasn't worth keeping now.

She became aware of someone walking beside her, his gait slightly halting, and looked up to see Toby.

"I thought your bonnet was the prettiest," he said diffidently. "Blue really suits you, Emmy."

Reality told her the old boater couldn't compare with Rose's bonnet and here was Toby saying he preferred it! She didn't know quite what to say, so just smiled up at him.

It might have been spitting with rain still, but it seemed a perfect spring day to Emmy as they strolled slowly along the lane.

She'd set the boater to dry in the kitchen while she made tea for Father and herself.

And Toby. She had a warm feeling that, in the days to come, she'd be making tea for him quite a lot. ■

Illustration by Pat Gregory.

The Hawthorn View

by Lydia Jones

NORA was aghast. Stepping down on to the patio with her mug of mid-morning coffee, her mouth dropped open.

Over the top of her garden fence four large wooden staves protruded so that the heavenly view up towards the hill topped by hawthorn trees – her view, as she thought of it – was divided into four sections, like one of those pictures that you buy in separate parts and have to hang together to make a whole.

Racing up to her box room, she peered down into the garden of the house backing on to hers and saw him: the new man with grey-peppered red hair and ingratiating smile.

"Good morning to you," he'd said that first day over the same fence. "I'm your new neighbour – Michael Byrne's my name."

He was a cliché of an Irishman with bright blue eyes; his smile suggested he might be inclined to linger.

"Morning," Nora had muttered, crossing her cardigan and moving back towards her own house. "And – er – welcome – of course."

As Nora now stared in dismay, Michael Byrne began to whistle, swinging his hammer in hand and poring over what looked like an instruction leaflet; his lawn was strewn with so many other pieces of timber Nora couldn't see grass.

Clearly he was building something monstrous. Something that would steal her patio view for ever. Nora turned away from the window and found her eyes were filled with tears.

*   *   *   *

"Well, why don't you ask him what he's building?"

Cathy from next door was chopping carrots.

"Oh, but it's none of my business."

"No offence, Nora, but you obviously think it is. If you're that bothered, love, speak to him about it. He seems a nice enough bloke.

"Heaven knows I've more to be worried about than whether or not I can see a few trees out of my back window."

Nora thought about Cathy's son who rode his motorbike so fast down the close and her girl whom she had seen at the bus stop dressed in what looked to Nora no more than a bra and knickers, and realised a vanishing view of the hawthorns could hardly be expected to matter much to Cathy.

"I think he's lovely," Lilian from the other side said. "He mended our fence for us. I've been asking Brian for ages but what with his back an' all –"

Obviously there was to be no neighbourly solidarity. But that didn't mean there was nothing Nora could do.

*   *   *   *

"Is it actually affecting light getting to your property?"

The clerk at the council offices looked over the top of her glasses.

"Well, no."

"Your walls? Will it impact on your foundations at all? Is the gentleman using it for purposes which create noise or disturbance?"

Nora felt foolish, crushed.

"If I were you I'd just have a quiet word."

"But he's almost finished building it."

Although she stopped short of actually saying, "What do you want me to do about it?", the clerk's face spoke volumes.

*   *   *   *

Nora's heart was pounding. She swallowed deliberately, pushed her shoulders down the way her mother had taught her and approached the fence.

Michael Byrne was sitting astride his grotesque timber skeleton unrolling a tube of black felt.

"Good morning." Nora's voice shook a little. She so hated confrontation; she hoped Mr Byrne wouldn't want one.

"Good morning to you, Mrs Tennyson-Wright. Your neighbour here, Cathy, now: she said your name was Nora. May I call you Nora, do you think?"

"Of course."

It wasn't the time to insist on formalities.

"Are you –?" How on earth to start? "Are you almost finished, then?"

Michael Byrne grinned wide enough to reach his red hairline.

"Just battling with the roofing felt, so I am. But it will be a fine summerhouse, though I say so myself. I'll be having a grand opening soon – thought I'd invite the neighbours round to share it."

"It's taken my view," Nora blurted out, unsure how to say it and bursting with the need to.

Michael Byrne looked puzzled. A troubled frown crossed his face.

"Of the hawthorns," Nora explained. "Up the hill."

"Can you not see them still?" He seemed perplexed. "I chose this kit because it didn't have one of those big pointy roofs like the others – didn't think you'd want that poking up over your back fence. Surely you still have the view from your back windows there?"

"Yes, but –" Nora fidgeted. "Not from my patio."

He looked down to the lowered rectangle of bricks by Nora's back door.

"I see. I'm sorry about that." He looked as if he genuinely were.

"How can I make it up to you, now? I'd thought to grow something over it – would you like to choose what? A Russian vine perhaps – if you're fond of white blossom. It's a bit like hawthorn, I think."

"No, thank you."

Something clamped hard around Nora's heart. It was gone for ever, then, her view. And he didn't understand, this man with the kind face and the appeasing smile. How could he?

Of course, it was still visible from her box room window, but how could she tell Michael Byrne that every morning for all the years since Archie had died, coffee on the patio had been a ritual?

Whatever the weather, sometimes under an umbrella, Nora had sipped sweet coffee, looked up to the hawthorns and remembered a time when she had lain beneath them and fallen in love.

Archie always said it was 1976.

"That long, hot, steamy summer," he'd say and then wink in that way that made her want to kiss him and swat him at the same time. But Nora knew it was 1975.

Back then Manchester University had been a real melting pot: a student community from all kinds of backgrounds.

"Archie," her husband had said back in the 1975 Student Union bar. He'd held out a hand in a formal greeting Nora had never before experienced. "Archie Tennyson-Wright."

Everything about Archie had been alien: from his aristocratic name to his race meetings and his monogrammed cufflinks. Alien and mesmerising.

When she'd taken him to meet her parents in the little terraced house in Stockport he had charmed them so completely it had stolen Nora's breath.

They'd taken a picnic up to the hawthorn hill to celebrate. The trees had been in full bloom that day.

"Did I pass muster, do you think?"

"You know fine well you did." Nora had giggled and leaned back against a hawthorn trunk.

"I'm glad." Archie had settled beside her. "Because you mean the world to me, my wonky-nosed woman."

"Cheek!"

She'd swatted his shoulder; they'd tussled playfully, kissed and then lay back on to the grass's soft bed and let the white petals fall on them like snow.

*   *   *   *

The door knock made her slop coffee into her saucer. She'd taken to drinking it by the box room window. But it wasn't the same.

The branches still looked bare from this distance, but Nora knew that up there cream buds would be burgeoning. Soon it would be hawthorn season and she wouldn't be able to see it. She sighed and went to open her door.

A bush of frothy white blossom stood on her doorstep carried by a pair of muscular freckled arms.

"Hello." Michael Byrne's head slanted to the side of it. He smiled cheerfully enough but his eyes were wary. Nora stepped aside to let him in. He shuffled, looking like an endearingly awkward adolescent.

"I've been feeling bad about what you told me. So I wondered –" He gave a throat-clearing little growl. "Would you like to come and have coffee in the summerhouse some time – when it's finished – with – er – me?"

"Oh – no, thank you," she said, startled, and then felt sorry for the look of hurt on his open face. "But thank you for asking – and for the plant, of course, though it wasn't necessary."

"You're welcome." His eyes still looked sad. "I'll be having a bit of a bash now – to christen the summerhouse. You'll come to that, won't you?"

*   *   *   *

Of course, not all the hawthorn memories were happy ones.

It was under those trees Archie had finally come clean about his gambling debts. The hawthorns had been in bud then: branches rippling overhead in the breeze like sheets of silken bubble wrap.

"You mean it all has to go?" Nora remembered nausea. "House? Car?"

"Everything." Archie had tugged up tufts of damp grass. "I'm sorry, Nora: all your lovely things. I've let you down. I'll understand if you want to wash your hands of me."

That had jerked her out of inertia.

"You silly man." She'd caressed his cheek, dashing away tears with an angry thumb. "You know I never wanted any of it: the big house; the Mercedes; the private school for Stephen. All I ever wanted was you."

So it had all been sold. Tenants of her parents' little terrace were given notice and Archie, Nora and Stephen had moved into the house with the hawthorn view.

Nora had got a good job and put herself in charge of their finances. Archie was allowed his "flutter money", which occasionally paid for treats, but mostly they'd lived a quiet life here in the house where Nora had grown up.

Stephen had flourished at the local school. He was a stockbroker now in London, where his father's penchant for risk-taking tempered by investment knowledge made him successful.

He had a lovely partner called Clifford who handled Nora's bemusement well. Once a year she travelled first class at their expense to spend Christmas in their tasteful apartment with the Thames view.

Nora knew she was blessed.

*   *   *   *

"You will go to this summerhouse launch thing, won't you?"

Lilian waved the home-printed invitation at Nora over their fence.

"I suppose it would be rude not to," Nora said.

For weeks now she'd watched the structure take shape from her window. Whenever he saw her Michael would wave. At first Nora always jumped back, but now she found her lips making a smile and her hand going up in a returned greeting.

Michael had festooned the little house with paper chains that reminded Nora of childhood Christmases. There was wine and crisps and little biscuits with cheese.

"Cheers!" Michael said. "And thank you all for coming."

"Thank you," Cathy said, looking more carefree than Nora had ever seen her. "For everything."

"What did she mean?" Nora whispered to Lilian as Cathy went to join her husband in admiring the structure.

"I expect she's glad about that motorbike engineering course Michael got her Jason into   working like mad at it, she says. And he got his daughter-in-law to give that flighty girl of Cathy's a Saturday job in her boutique."

Lilian rose to join the others out in the garden. Nora sat in one of the summerhouse's little wicker chairs and looked up at her hawthorns rippling in all their early summer glory.

Without being there, she could still smell their fragrance, imagine the feel of the falling petals on her skin, hear the creaking of the branches swaying in the breeze.

"Penny for them?"

Suddenly Michael was beside her.

Nora gave a little breathy laugh.

"I was just thinking everybody's summer seems to be looking up."

"Not yours?" He frowned. "Oh, by the way – I meant to give you this. It's a sunflower – or will be – I've grown too many from seed."

"Sunflowers – they were my husband's favourite," Nora said softly.

"A man with an eye for a fine flower, then." Michael nodded. "And a fine woman, too, if it's not too corny to say so."

Nora laughed again: twice now in the space of as many moments. She couldn't remember the last time that had happened.

"It is corny – but thank you anyway – I think."

There was a pause while they both stared up at the hawthorns.

"I meant it, you know: I'd be glad if you would come and share the view – any time."

"Why are you so nice to me?" she asked. "What do you want from me?"

His blue eyes flared wide with surprise and then he chuckled.

"Well, I do like a woman who comes to the point." He shrugged. "Your friendship, Nora. I should like it very much if we could be friends.

"I'm sorry about stealing your view and I'll make it up to you – if you don't mind sharing your coffee with me sometimes. I'm –" He swallowed hard. "I'm a little lonely, you see."

"I'm lonely, too," she said, realising in that moment that it was true.

"Will we share the view of the hawthorns sometimes then, this summer?" He still looked uncertain.

"Why not?" she said, all at once feeling more light-hearted than she had done for a long time.

She had spent too many hours living in the past, the view of her beloved hawthorn trees rooting her there. Perhaps now they could help her take a tiny step forward into the future.

"To the hawthorn view."

Michael raised his wine glass.

"The hawthorn view."

Nora sipped her wine and smiled. A view really was much better for being shared. ■

Stock and Alamy.

Memorable Music

JOSEPH EASTBURN WINNER, a Philadelphia composer, published a little ditty in 1869 that has remained in circulation ever since. "Little Brown Jug" tells the story of a couple who have fallen on hard times because of their fondness for the demon drink, yet they're happy because they have each other.

The catchy chorus, "Ha ha ha, you and me, little brown jug, don't I love thee", helped the song to become a hit from coast to coast.

The sheet music sold well and when recordings came on the scene, artists were keen to add it to their repertoire. Glenn Miller and his Orchestra recorded the song in 1939 and Rosemary Clooney sang the song with Bing Crosby in 1952. It has even been referenced by Kate Bush in one of the tracks on her 2005 album, "Aerial".

Serious music also saw a significant addition in this year, when Richard Wagner's opera "Das Rheingold", the first in the Ring Cycle, received its first performance in Munich on September 22. ■

Paper Ladies

by Isobel J. Sayer

HANG on, Pippa, let me check my diary." Tess put the handset down as she rummaged in the drawer underneath the telephone table. For once she hadn't had to go on a hunt for the phone; usually she had to try to find it before whoever was calling got fed up and rang off.

Tess was often to be heard reminiscing about the days when a good old-fashioned telephone was attached to the wall; one which recalcitrant teenagers could not disappear off with into the depths of a bedroom, not to be found until the battery was long discharged and the lonely base unit was heard ringing forlornly without its most vital component!

Tess sifted through numerous pizza and Chinese take-away leaflets, finally finding her diary and a pen underneath a dog-eared phone book.

"Tuesday morning?" she queried while flipping to the correct week. "Well, I normally have Pilates but I can easily give that a miss next week. No, honestly, darling, it's fine; I know the struggle with school holidays."

She nodded and mouthed "Pippa" at Jim, who had just appeared at the kitchen doorway holding up the teapot with his eyebrows raised.

"Sorry, darling, what time did you say you'll drop her off? OK. And Harvey is going to a friend for the day? You know I don't mind having them both if it's easier. No problem, see you Tuesday. Don't work too hard."

Jim smiled at her.

"Kettle's just boiling."

Tess placed the phone back into its charger, crossed out *Pilates* and scribbled *Ella 0900* in large letters across the previous entry.

"I'm babysitting Ella on Tuesday," she called out. "Pip's got some work thing that she's on a deadline with."

Jim brought a mug through to the lounge and held it out to her. He indicated the brightly coloured tin on the coffee table.

"Do you want a slice of your fruitcake with that?"

Tessa enjoyed baking and made extremely good cakes. She sighed as she patted her midriff.

"I probably shouldn't."

Jim came up behind her and put his arms around her.

"Who cares about a bit of middle-aged spread? I love you just the way you are," he reminded her. "Anyway, I've just had two pieces, so you have to eat at

Illustration by Helen Welsh.

least one or you'll make me feel greedy.

"What are you going to do with the children, then, love?"

"It's only Ella this time. Harvey's off playing with a friend. I thought maybe if the weather's good, there's that lovely little playground not far from here. We might bake something together, too." She laughed ruefully. "More goodies to tempt us away from our healthy-eating resolve."

✳　✺　✳　✢

Pippa dashed in from the car, dripping on the porch as she extracted seven-year-old Ella from her red- and black-spotted raincoat with the ladybird hood.

"Wellies, Ella! Come on, I'm running late because you took so long getting ready to go."

"Here, let Nana do it." Tess took over, easing the little girl out of the wet coat. "You get on, Pip. Drive carefully and don't work too hard."

Jim appeared and helped Ella with her boots.

"I wanted my ladybird boots and Mummy couldn't find them, so I had to wear Harvey's smelly froggy boots," she grumbled. "They're too huge for me, and they made me trip over into a puddle, and look, Grandad." She pointed out a tiny graze on her knee for his inspection.

"Here, let me kiss it better and put a special bandage on it."

Ella sat on the floor just inside the door as Jim pulled a neatly ironed white handkerchief out of his pocket and tied it loosely just above her knee.

Ella limped dramatically into the lounge and flopped herself down on to a

71

beanbag. Tess held out her hand.

"Do you want to help make my special caramel oaty slice?"

Injured knee forgotten, Ella jumped up from the beanbag and put her hand into Tess's. Tess was sure she would never tire of the feeling, and would often instigate a walk with the children just to have a trusting little hand in hers once again.

"You can scrape the bowl when we've finished," Tess promised as she thwarted a sneaky dip into the bowl of crumble mixture. "Now sit tight where you are while I do the caramel. It's very, very hot."

Ella sat obediently on her tall kitchen stool and watched as Tess poured the hot sauce on to the oat base before letting her granddaughter scrape the rest of the mixture on top and pat it down with a spoon.

With the baking safely in the oven, Tess glanced out of the kitchen window. The rain still poured down outside with no sign of stopping.

With the washing-up done, and reluctance on her part to put the television on, she dithered somewhat about how to entertain a lively seven-year-old girl.

"Let me show you my Minecraft, Grandad." Ella rummaged in a pink flowery backpack and pulled out her iPad.

"I have no idea what you're talking about, poppet, but sure, come and show me." Jim put down the newspaper crossword. "Two down, seven letters, ends in S, the clue is 'where to find someone to speak to'."

"Address," Tess said without really stopping to think. She had a knack for cryptic crosswords.

Jim nodded and pencilled it in just before his beloved granddaughter climbed on to his lap, her tablet playing some sort of repetitive electronic music.

Tess reminded him of the subject of Ella's current fascination with this modern electronic game.

"It's that strange building game, Jim. Don't you remember – she's been building you a house next to her hotel! I think you had pigs on your roof garden last week." She chuckled.

*   *   *   *

"Mum, you're a star as always." Pippa had the same warm smile as her father; their matching brown eyes sparkled. It never failed to tug at Tess's heart to see how alike her daughter and husband were.

The grandchildren took after their son-in-law more in looks, fair-haired with blue eyes.

Ella solemnly held out a plastic tub containing caramel oat slices.

"Me and Nana did cooking, Mummy."

Pippa lifted a corner of the lid and inhaled the scent of warm baking.

"My favourite. Thanks, Mum."

"I was struggling to think of ways to entertain her today. She's really

Rainy Days

RAIN! Rain! Rain!
Clouds drift dark and grey;
Roses hang their heavy heads,
Soggy as they sway;
Lawns squelch sodden underfoot,
Mist obscures the view,
Droplets cling like gossamer
To dampen one all through.
The weeds, however, flourish,
Bursting forth with zest,
Crowding blooms in gardens –
Smothering the rest;
Growing tall, they might exclaim
"There's no substitute for weeds!
With the help of bird and wind,
We've scattered all our seeds!"

Dawn Lawrence.

outgrown the box of toys we have here, Pip. Is there anything you have at home that you could leave here for her?"

She absentmindedly smoothed down the small head in front of her.

"We did get out for that walk in the end, though, didn't we, Ella? That poorly knee was soon forgotten."

Pippa finished buttoning up the raincoat, glancing across at her young son sitting patiently in the car to avoid the drizzle coming down outside.

"I've got a couple of boxes of my old things in the loft; I'll bring them over, let you sort through them, Mum, if you don't mind. You can sift out the stuff that I should have thrown out years ago, and put aside anything you think that the children might like to play with at your house."

*　*　*　*

Tess sat on the lounge floor sifting through memories as she sorted the boxes dropped off the evening before by their daughter.

She made several piles of toys: keep, throw away, and some for the charity shop. A selection of Barbie dolls, along with sets of clothing and pairs of tiny shoes, a box of Fuzzy-Felt, Spirograph and a collection of Teenage Mutant Turtle figurines all went into the stack to save for the children to play with.

There were battered boxes containing games of "Guess Who" with all the

iStock.

pieces intact, and "Mousetrap", which she would get Jim to build and make sure it was all there.

Tess dug deep into the bottom of the last box and pulled out a large plastic tub.

"Jim, do you remember this?"

Jim shifted his gaze from the cricket match on TV and smiled.

"She loved making those with you." He held out his hand to take the item Tess was showing him. "I remember it well; I didn't think Pip would have kept them for all these years!"

"Do you think Ella would like to make some?" Tess then looked doubtful. "Maybe not. After all, children are so much into everything being electronic these days."

Jim studied the home-made toy and accessories Tess handed him.

"Well, we promised the children they could come over on Saturday. I could finish that bird box with Harvey. And if your idea is too old-fashioned for Ella, well, once we've condensed Pippa's old toys into one big box, there'll be plenty of new things for her to play with!"

"Fair enough. I'll ring Pippa and get her to pack a few of Ella's favourite clothes, just in case." Tess disappeared to rummage in a cupboard in the study.

She carefully added a flattened cereal box and some sheets of plain paper from the printer to the contents of the plastic tub before ringing her daughter with her rather strange request.

Even if her find didn't inspire a modern seven-year-old to do something crafty, Tess felt that Pippa might like to see what she had found from her childhood of nearly 30 years ago.

*   *   *   *

"Mum, I'm intrigued to know what it is you're planning." Pippa dropped the two excited grandchildren at the front door early the next Saturday morning.

"You'll find out later, so long as Ella doesn't think it's too old-fashioned."

"I'll get back to our decorating now, if you don't mind, Mum. I've left Patrick doing the undercoating; hopefully we'll have Harvey's room painted and it will be dry before he gets home."

With Harvey and Jim happily ensconced in the garage, Tess sat at the kitchen breakfast bar with Ella and opened the plastic box. Lifting out the now slightly fragile items, she laid them out in front of her.

"Your mum and I made these when she was about your age."

"Wow, can we make one, Nana?" Ella's eyes were shining, all thoughts of television and her iPad forgotten.

"I hoped you might say that; come and see what your mum packed us for inspiration."

Tessa opened the backpack and pulled out a blue and white floaty party dress, with sparkles on the tulle skirt. This was followed by Ella's grey school trousers and red sweatshirt.

Ella looked into the bag, pulling out one garment after another.

"All my favourite clothes and my best rabbit pyjamas."

I hope I'm up to drawing rabbits, Tess thought quietly, as the sound of their cutting out and colouring mingled with faint drilling and hammering coming from the garage.

*   *   *   *

"Mummy, Daddy, come and see what me and Ella made!" Harvey declared.

The wooden bird box was duly admired from every angle. Ella sat, surprisingly quiet, a grin on her face, eyes shining, waiting her turn.

"What did you and Nana make?" Pippa queried.

Ella carefully drew out a handmade cardboard doll. She had yellow hair in two bunches tied in ribbons, and bright blue eyes.

Ella stood the doll up on a little stand and smoothed down the tabs on the paper outfit which they had made to match Ella's school uniform.

"See, Mummy, we had to make tabs to hold her clothes on." She turned the doll round to show Pippa the back, not at all bothered about exposing the cornflake packet which was used to make her.

"We made lots of outfits for her, even some pyjamas. Nana can draw really good bunny rabbits, Mum."

Pippa took the doll and admired their handiwork before turning to Tess.

"Didn't we make one of these when I was little?"

Tess handed Pippa the plastic container and grinned.

"She's in there; all the clothes are still there, too, a bit tatty now, but it was all in the bottom of one of those boxes you gave me."

Pippa drew out a similar doll dressed in a slightly faded red and blue frock with piped pockets on the skirt.

"Oh, my word, Mum! I remember that dress; I practically lived in it until I grew out of it!" She knelt down next to her daughter. "Well, I think these two paper ladies should go somewhere special in their outfits, don't you?"

"Pizza Hut!" the two children chorused.

"I don't see why not," Patrick agreed as they headed excitedly for the door. He turned to Jim and Tess. "Thank you so much, you two. It's our turn to entertain them now. At least going out for dinner with them will give that last coat of paint a chance to dry!"

Pippa gave her mum a kiss.

"Thanks, Mum, you're a star; you've really taken me back with this." She popped the paper ladies back into the box and carefully closed the lid.

"You taught me how to be a good mother, and you're already showing me how to be a great nana when my turn comes." ■

Castlefield Canal Basin, Manchester

CASTLEFIELD derives its name from its position below the former Roman fort of Mancunium, which gave its name to Manchester, and was formerly known as Castle-in-the-field.

The Bridgewater Canal arrived in Castlefield around the time of the Industrial Revolution, having been commissioned by Francis Egerton, 3rd Duke of Bridgewater, who was keen to transport coal from his mines in Worsley to Manchester. The area became a thriving hub of engineering works and busy warehouses, but when these fell into decline, the basin was regenerated and the warehouses adapted for modern use.

It's hard to imagine how different the area would have looked in the past-, and boat trips now deliver historical commentary for tourists keen to explore the area. ■

Illustration by Kirk Houston.

A Nudge In The Right Direction

by Pamela Ormondroyd

O H, hi, Mum. It's me, Julie. How's things?"
My daughter doesn't give me time to reply but hurries on.
"Only I need to ask a huge favour of you. I've been left in the lurch, you see. Brenda Philips isn't able to help with the Teddy Bears' Picnic tomorrow and I've now got three little girls looking for a nice, kind lady to look after them. Any chance you might be free?"

I sigh. Julie knows I'll be free. Aren't I always, these days? And being caught on the hop like this means I haven't the time to think up any credible excuse.

"Um, well, I er . . ."

Oh, dear, I'm well and truly trapped!

"It's only for the morning, Mum," Julie continues, pressing her advantage. "We go to Lark Wood, take a little stroll around, have a picnic with our bears and then the children go on the play park for a while.

"And the little girls I've earmarked for you are a delight, truthfully. I'd be so grateful."

Well, that's that, then. Julie knows I'd never let her down when it comes to the playgroup.

I mean, if I'm being completely honest, I don't really feel like going out anywhere, but . . .

"Yes, all right, I'll come," I say, feeling weary even as I speak. "What time?"

After the instructions I sit down to think. The last time I walked in Lark Wood, my darling Ted was by my side.

He had his arm through mine because he was growing weaker by then and needed my support, so we took it slowly and we managed to have a lovely day. We even spent some time looking for the woodpecker who regularly nested there.

But memories, beautiful though they are, can still make me tearful, so I take myself off to the kitchen to check that I've enough bread to make a sandwich for the picnic.

And since it's only early summer, I reckon it might be a little cool under the trees in Lark Wood, so I'll need to pop upstairs and dig out a thick jumper and my walking shoes.

$$* \quad * \quad * \quad *$$

The following morning I wake up to bright sunshine which lifts my mood, though I do confess to feeling a little nervous as I pick up my bag.

I haven't had much to do with tiny children for nearly a year since I retired, and I don't know any of the playgroup parents.

No doubt Julie will be busy organising everything, too, so I'll be on my own most of the time.

I take a deep breath and lift my chin.

Well, I'll just have to concentrate on my three little charges, then. I'm sure they'll be very excited and happy to chatter on non-stop.

When I present myself at the church hall, a coach is already parked up outside and inside, 25 little bodies are being fastened into their coats, given last-minute instructions and labelled.

Julie looks up from fitting two tiny hands into a pair of gloves and waves.

"Oh, hi, Mum." She smiles. "Ramona and Kylie are over there at the corner table. Ella couldn't come because she's got a cold so you've only got two girls."

Two pretty little faces, one framed by long golden hair and the other by two shiny brown bunches tied up with red bows, stare at me with a slightly puzzled air.

"This is Mrs Drake. Do you remember I told you about her yesterday?" Julie says. "Mrs Philips couldn't come so Mrs Drake is going to look after you both this morning."

After a few moments spent sizing me up, the children feel confident enough to tell me what they had for breakfast and to show me what's inside their lunch boxes.

Then they introduce me to their respective teddy bears.

Ramona with the golden hair has brought along a tiny little scrawny fellow with one ear.

"He's called Cuddles," she says proudly.

Then Kylie scoops up a large, well-fed looking chap from the floor beneath her chair and virtually throws him into my lap.

"He's Bert," she says. " He keeps me warm in bed."

I open my shoulder bag and produce my own little specimen.

"This is Eric," I tell them.

The little girls scrutinise their new elderly companion with unruly grey hair, holding up her own teddy bear, and express a sense of bewilderment.

Eric looks as ancient as me with odd buttons for eyes, a patch on his arm, no visible fur and a lop-sided grin.

"Is that really yours?" Ramona asks.

I nod. Well, he is now. Actually he was Ted's old bear, presented to him by a very proud mother on his very first birthday.

Eric, over 70 years, has been party to all the ups and downs, the happiness and sadness, of one family's entire life.

Now this little fellow is a comfort to me when I reach out for Ted on the long, cold, lonely nights.

*   *   *   *

We are ready; Julie, the children, the playgroup assistants and the young parent-helpers.

I take the girls' hands and we walk up the coach steps, but for a moment, once boarded, I stop and look around.

As I thought, I don't know anyone and have no idea where to sit. All the young parents are matched up and I wouldn't like to seem too forward and plonk myself down just anywhere.

"You're up near the front, Mum." Julie is behind me.

Oh, Julie, dear Julie. My daughter's been at my side and behind me all the way through. Supporting, guiding, gently nudging.

"I've put you in that seat across the aisle, next to Mr Graham."

I look for a Mr Graham and see a white-haired chap waving at me. He's squeezed on to a seat with two little boys.

I usher Ramona and Kylie forward and we all three squeeze on to the adjacent seat.

"You got roped in, too, then, Julie's mum?" Mr Graham smiles. Then he points to the two little boys next to him.

"Freddie, my grandson, and his little pal, Tyler," he says. "Bit of a handful, both of them together, so I thought I should lend a hand. Well, it's a lovely day for it."

The coach starts up and we are soon on our way. My two young charges hold their teddies up to the window and show them all the sights as we travel along.

I sit back and place my head on the rest. I don't want to seem rude but I don't feel like making conversation, even though Mr Graham seems to have other ideas.

He tells me he used to go to Lark Wood a lot at one time, first with his wife in their courting days and then with their children and now with his grandchildren. But now he's on his own, he doesn't do much walking far from home.

Suddenly, I'm a bit cross with Julie. What does she think she's doing, putting me next to the only elderly gentleman on the coach?

She knows I'm not up for polite conversation with strangers, even if they do mean well. I just don't feel like answering questions or opening up about myself.

So, I just smile and cut Mr Graham short and then I turn to talk to the girls and just hope he isn't offended.

Coping with small children is enough for me at the moment because everything is on a simple level with them.

I mean, I only lost Ted seven months ago and I'm not the happy-go-lucky person I used to be. I'm different, somehow, and my world has changed.

*   *   *   *

Luckily, the coach trip was only short and we have arrived at the wood and are now walking in the fresh air.

I feel free again, more normal. I was beginning to feel a bit claustrophobic on the coach.

The bluebells are just on the turn, but fresh green leaves are rustling overhead and the air is full of birdsong.

And Mr Graham has his hands full watching the boys as they tear on ahead, so Ramona and Kylie and I seek out rabbit holes and watch squirrels scuttling up the tree trunks.

Now and again we link arms and listen out for the woodpecker, but he's not around today. I take deep breaths. I always found that the wood used to calm

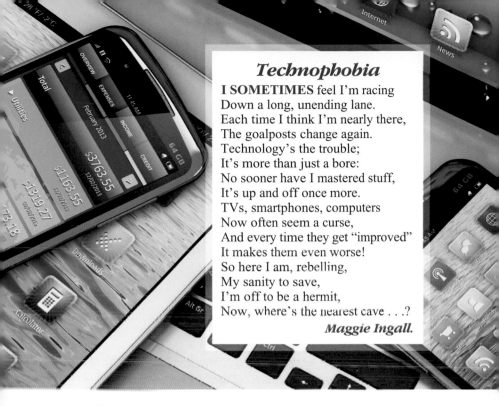

Technophobia

I SOMETIMES feel I'm racing
Down a long, unending lane.
Each time I think I'm nearly there,
The goalposts change again.
Technology's the trouble;
It's more than just a bore:
No sooner have I mastered stuff,
It's up and off once more.
TVs, smartphones, computers
Now often seem a curse,
And every time they get "improved"
It makes them even worse!
So here I am, rebelling,
My sanity to save,
I'm off to be a hermit,
Now, where's the nearest cave . . .?

Maggie Ingall.

me and it still does.

I feel lighter, more at peace. I guess my caring daughter knew I would. And I sense now that one day I probably will come back and find that woodpecker again.

*   *   *   *

Soon, it's lunchtime, and Julie rolls out a giant rug and we all sit down in a circle with our teddies.

Mr Graham and his two charges sit almost opposite us, but I carefully avoid his gaze and focus on my two little girls. They really are quite loveable. In fact, all the children are.

Afterwards, they are allowed to play on the equipment in the park and when we finally get back on to the coach, Ramona rests her head on my shoulder and falls asleep while Kylie looks up and says she's had a lovely day and that she likes me.

I realise how much I've missed working with small children. Their innocence and enthusiasm is so uplifting.

Maybe I will offer to read to the playgroup children now and again, or help with artwork. To be honest, I think they'll help me as much, if not more, than I do them.

iStock.

I'm suddenly aware of a few young mums chatting a few seats up from mine.

"I thought Brenda Philips was coming with us today," one of them says. Then another chips in.

"No, apparently Julie told her she already had enough helpers," she says. "So she wasn't needed."

I smile to myself. Another contrived but gentle nudge from Julie to ease me back into the light.

I look back and see her squeezed up on the back seat with about six little children. They're singing away with all their teddies dancing on their knees, and I feel so proud of her.

She is so good with children and I was so lucky to have been blessed with such a daughter. In fact, I was blessed with both Ted and her, and instead of feeling sorry for myself I know I should be eternally grateful.

Julie lost her beloved father, too, yet she's picked herself up and carried on and, hard as it is, I do realise that I have to do the same.

The coach comes to a halt and Mr Graham gets up and doffs his cap.

"Nice to meet you, Julie's mum," he says.

"It's Sylvie," I say, looking up. "Nice to meet you, too."

"Fred." He winks. Then he taps me gently on the shoulder as he passes. "It does get easier, you know."

And then he is lost in the mêlée of mums, dads and tired little folk.

How does Mr Graham know about me and my circumstances? Did he perhaps recognise in me the sadness that he himself might have carried at one time?

Or did my Julie tell him?

*   *   *   *

Back at home, I sit on the edge of the bed, put Eric on the chair next to it and reflect.

I knew there would be good and bad days, but I would say that, overall, today has been a good one. A much better one, in fact, even though it got off to a bit of a shaky start.

Although there was a time I didn't think it possible, today I actually feel part of the real world again. It hasn't changed at all, just my perception of it. And I'm still me.

One day, my own grandchildren may arrive. Julie and her husband have already indicated that they would like to start a family soon, and I agree that the time feels right now.

And if that day does come, old Eric will hopefully be given a new lease of life.

And so, with luck and a daughter's love, shall I! ∎

iStock.

Entering History

THE history of the world was altered with the birth on October 2, 1869, of Mohandas Karamchand Gandhi. Gandhi would later leave his home in Gujarat to train in law at the Inner Temple in London before practising as a barrister.

In South Africa, he became involved in non-violent civil disobedience in support of the civil rights of the local Indian community. Once he returned to India, he introduced the technique to the movement protesting against unfair taxes and discrimination imposed by the British Raj, which eventually led to India's independence in 1947.

Other notable births in this year were Henry Wood, born March 3, who became a celebrated conductor and was the founder of the Proms; Edward Lutyens, born March 29, who designed the Cenotaph at Whitehall and was instrumental in the design of New Delhi in India and is now regarded as one of the great British architects of the twentieth century; and Lady Constance Bulwer-Lytton, born January 12, a suffragette and an influential writer, speaker, and campaigner for prison reform. ■

The Way To His Heart

by Pamela Kavanagh

WHEN the church committee chose our Annie to make the gingerbread for the St Anne's Day Rushbearing Ceremony this coming July, I wondered what all the fuss was about. Like any other Ambleside lad, I knew about the custom, all right; how it harked back to the days of strewing the church with rushes when floors were nothing but beaten earth.

These days the rushbearers parade through the streets led by the town band, ending up at the Market Place where the old Rushbearing hymn is sung.

We all go on to the church, and after the service each rushbearer is given a piece of gingerbread. I should think they probably need it after all that marching, and then having to sit through one of Parson's lengthy sermons.

"Fancy," Mam said. "Our Annie, making the gingerbread. Well!"

Pleased as Punch, was Mam, though Annie was frowning.

"Why me?" she said.

"Happen it's because of your name being the same as the saint's."

"But it ain't. She's Annie, not Anne," I chipped in from where I sat, whittling a model of a cock pheasant from a scrap of beech filched from Father's woodshed.

"Who's she, my lad, the cat's mother?" Mam said sharply.

Being the youngest of the brood, I tended to get the sharp edge of Mam's tongue, and Annie's warm brown gaze was sympathetic as it fell on me.

"I'm Annie in the way that you're Billie. I was baptised Anne, like the saint, but I became Annie. You were named William but you get called Billie," she explained with customary patience. "See?"

I shrugged and went back to my whittling. None of it made much sense to me but then at ten-and-a-quarter, the ways of grown-ups rarely did.

"Gingerbread," Annie said on a sigh.

The word shivered around our cluttered houseplace like a dreaded breath of wintry wind. Cooking was not Annie's best-liked occupation.

Oh, don't get me wrong. Annie could turn out a tasty beef stew and a loaf of bread as good as anyone, but when it came to fancier fare she did not have what Mam called the lightest of hands.

Illustration by iStock.

"You'd best look lively, Annie, if you want your gingerbread to be as good as Janice Coles's was last year," Mam cautioned. This was followed by the usual mantra. "Make no mistake, the way to a fellow's heart is through his stomach. We can't have the likes of that one beating you to the altar."

It was only the end of June and St Anne's Day wasn't until the 26th of next month, which left plenty of time to get sorted. I was prepared to forget the whole bothersome issue and concentrate on increasing my range of bird models, which largely depended upon gaining access to Father's wood store.

But seeing the worried look on Annie's face, I thought twice. She was a good sort, our Annie. As the eldest she'd had a hand in bringing us all up.

I had once overheard her confiding to her friend Belinda that she was sweet on Sam Woodridge, the under-gardener at Major Landbuck's place, and Janice Coles was setting her cap at him.

Annie was my big sister and goodness itself. Surely I could find some way to repay her for all her past kindnesses?

* * * *

Well, I mulled the matter over, but nothing popped into my mind. So I did the usual thing whenever a problem remained stubbornly unresolved and clicked my fingers to Gyp.

We headed for the woods, me whistling tunelessly, the terrier scampering along on his stubby legs, his senses alert for something to chase in the undergrowth.

We had reached a fork in the track when Gyp made a dive for a holly thicket and disappeared. There was a cry, a hysterical woofing.

"Gyp, come here!" I hollered.

The barking continued and heedless of the prickles I barged, whooping and yelling threats, into the bushes to investigate the kerfuffle.

Gyp was jumping up at his quarry – a girl of around my own age who I recognised as Major Landbuck's eldest. She was all golden ringlets and ruffles.

Her white pinafore bore the imprint of muddy paws, but at least she was unharmed. She gave a breathless little laugh.

"Oh, please don't be cross with him. He wasn't doing anything, not really. I was just startled when he appeared like that."

She put out a hand to Gyp, letting him sniff her palm, his stump of a tail wagging frantically.

Anyone who was all right by Gyp was all right by me, but I was cautious. The Landbucks were gentry. It was not usual to find one of them all alone in the woods.

I cleared my throat.

"You're Miss Alice, ain't you? I'm Billie Merriday, from the woodyard." This gave me a certain status, since everyone including the major sourced their timber from Merriday's Yard.

She smiled, two dimples like our Annie's appearing in her cheeks.

"Pleased to meet you, Billie. Gyp, too. I'd love a dog but Mama says I must wait until my brothers are bigger."

"A dog would guard you. Especially here in the woods."

A look of horror crossed her face.

"You won't tell anyone you've seen me, will you? I like to come here and watch the birds." She pointed to a stately beech. "There's a nest in the trunk of that tree. The baby birds come out and crawl along the branches."

I spotted one; small, brown-backed, white-breasted, bobbing up the tree trunk like a tiny feathery mouse.

"Them's treecreepers," I told her, pleased to know something that she plainly did not.

"Treecreepers." She spoke the name wonderingly. "It certainly describes them, doesn't it? I could watch them all day. But I suppose I should really be getting back, before I'm missed."

"Don't they know you're gone?"

"Dear me, no. Susannah thinks I'm reading a book in the garden. Susannah's the nursery maid. She's really nice. She doesn't get cross like Nanny. I don't suppose you'd care to walk back with me? It's lovely to have someone to talk to."

Being short of a natter was never a problem at our house and I felt an unexpected stab of sympathy for Miss Alice.

We fell into step, Gyp scampering ahead, and as we went I explained about Annie's dilemma. Miss Alice listened carefully until I came to a stumbling conclusion.

"Our Annie is sweet on Sam Woodridge, see, and Mam says the way to his heart is by being able to cook real good. I wouldn't want Janice Coles to get her claws into him."

"No, I do see that. I know Sam. He digs our garden and prunes the roses. He does other things, too, like playing the fiddle in the town band."

"Papa says he'll go a long way – but I don't want him to go anywhere. I'd far rather he stayed here and married your sister."

"Not much chance of that, knowing our Annie's baking," I said gloomily.

Miss Alice considered the matter, her forehead crinkling.

"If that's the way to his heart, as your mama says, we need a plan. Gingerbread can't be terribly hard to make. If you like, I'll ask Susannah to get the recipe from Cook. Cook's gingerbread is truly delicious."

"Could you? I wouldn't want you to get a skelping."

She giggled.

"Skelping! What a lovely word. Never fear, Billie, I shall be mindful not to get into trouble. Ah, here we are."

We had reached the tall boundary wall of the big house. After making arrangements to meet the following day by the treecreepers' beech, I watched her clamber nimbly up the ancient ivy that cloaked the wall and disappear over the top in a flurry of petticoats.

*   *   *   *

The next afternoon she was waiting for me when I turned up with Gyp, the pair of us panting from the run through the leafy tunnels of trees.

"Here you are." Triumphantly she handed me a folded slip of paper. "Susannah said there could be a secret ingredient that makes all the difference to the taste."

"So what is it?"

Miss Alice gave me a look of reproof.

"Silly! If I knew that, it wouldn't be a secret, would it? According to Susannah, recipes get passed down from one generation to the next and people have their own ways of making things special. I expect that will be the secret ingredient."

"D'you reckon that's why Janice Coles's gingerbread went down so well at last year's Rushbearing Ceremony?"

"It could be. If you were a bird in a tree, like the treecreeper, you could keep watch and find out what she puts into her baking."

It was meant as a jest, but after we had watched the treecreepers' antics for a while, and as repayment for her trouble I'd shown her where a vixen brought out her cubs, I got to thinking.

School was over for now. Nobody ever turned up at haysel, since with most of the children helping their folks on the harvest fields it was scarcely worth schoolmaster Mr Wainbridge opening the doors.

Once I had swept the yards for Father – my job, since on leaving school I was to be apprenticed to the trade – I had all day to myself.

"Got an idea," I said abruptly.

She heard me out, that frown of concentration on her face. Then she smiled.

"Splendid. You will let me know how you get on?"

"Course I will. Oh, and thanks for the recipe, miss."

"You're welcome. And do call me Alice in future. You're Billie, I'm Alice. That's only fair."

"All right then, Alice," I said boldly.

*　　*　　*　　*

"Where did you get this?" Annie asked, after studying the recipe.

"A friend found it for me." I shrugged it off, and Annie seemed to accept that. I supposed Alice could be termed a friend, even if she was a girl.

First, I had to see how Janice Coles went about her cookery, and leaving Annie making a list of requirements for the gingerbread, I left the house.

Across the lane from the Coles's cottage was a spreading sycamore. It was no problem to climb up and settle down on a bough. Here, I had a prime view of everything.

Janice was in the garden, her nose in a novelette. Mouth-watering smells issued from the open window of the kitchen, where someone, probably Janice's mam, could be heard beating a mixture with a wooden spoon.

After a while, Mrs Coles appeared in the doorway.

"Janice? The raspberry sponge is done. Can you can take it and leave it on the step?"

Janice put aside her book, pouting.

"If I must."

"'Twill be in your interest, my girl. You know what they say about the way to a fellow's heart?"

I frowned. If this was what I thought, the offering was definitely not the result of Janice's labours.

She disappeared into the cottage and emerged again carrying the cake wrapped in a red-checked cloth, and set off along the lane.

Slithering down the tree, I followed at a distance. The holding where Sam lived was set off the road, a low-roofed dwelling with a cobbled yard and outbuildings.

There was an orchard, and a well-tended garden. I could picture Annie here, scattering grain to her hens and growing herbs for the kitchen.

Janice left the cake on the front step and hurried off, back to her novelette.

The next day I was at my sentry post again. This time it was cherry scones, and the day after that it was plum cake.

"It seems to me there's some skulduggery going on," I said to Alice when we met by the treecreepers' beech.

Alice nodded.

"That Janice Coles is cheating for sure. If the same happened with the gingerbread last year, she won all that praise under false pretences."

"My thoughts exactly. The thing is, Alice, what's to be done about it?"

She bit her lip, thoughts chasing across her violet-blue eyes.

"You had better leave this to me," she said at last.

*   *   *   *

Evening was here before I could head off for the Coles's cottage. Voices raised in argument met me as I approached the lane.

"What's gingerbread to do with anything?"

That was Janice; accusing, indignant.

"Just tell me straight. Did you make it yourself or not? Because if what's come to my attention is right, you've not been playing fair, Janice Coles."

I crept into the bushes, inching forward to peer through the branches. Janice and Sam stood by the gate to Sam's holding. Guilty colour suffused Janice's cheeks and Sam was no fool.

"You're a cheat, Janice. You'd best get off home, and be thankful this will go no further!"

Janice's face flamed all the more.

"All right, I'm going. And you can get back to your garden, Sam Woodridge, because that's all you're fit for. No girl wants to come second to a few miserable flowers and cabbages!"

Furiously wrenching a rose from the bush that rambled over the fence, Janice tore it apart and flung it down at Sam's feet, before flouncing off in high dudgeon along the lane.

Sam, having just returned from a long day at Major Landbuck's, shook his head wearily and carried on to his house, closing the door behind him.

*   *   *   *

"It worked, then," Alice said, dimpling. "I thought it might."

It seemed she had enlisted the help of the nursery maid and asked Susannah to have a word with Sam, which was good thinking on Alice's part.

"Now all that remains is for someone to put in a word for Annie," I said.

"Oh, that's easy," Alice replied. "Sam's best-liked flower is the rose. You might tell Annie to wear a spray in her bonnet on St Anne's Day. Sam's sure to spot her when he goes by in the band."

"And after that?"

Alice looked at me wisely.

"We've done our best, Billie. The rest is up to them."

*   *   *   *

Annie's preference for leaving flowers to their own devices in the garden was legendary and she took some persuading to pluck a spray of buds from the pink rose that clustered around our front porch.

But she gave in good-naturedly, and Mam nodded in approval at the picture she made in her new sprigged muslin and rose-adorned headgear.

Even after the rebuff he had received, shy, unassuming Sam noticed my sister all right as the band led the rushbearers through Ambleside.

During the service at the church, Alice sent me a secretive wave from the pew where she sat with her parents and three small brothers.

Service over, I expect her fingers were crossed as tightly as mine as Annie nervously made her offering of gingerbread.

It seemed to go down a treat and Mam let out an audible sigh of relief.

Later, Sam sought Annie out.

"Them's bonnie roses in your bonnet, Annie. Tes Maiden's Blush, if I'm not mistaken?"

The heightened colour in Annie's cheeks perfectly reflected the name of the rose.

"Why, yes, I believe it is. Father planted it for Mam on their first anniversary. It's a pretty thing and sweetly scented, too."

"Fond of roses, are you?"

"Very," Annie said, and with habitual honesty she went on, "and that's more than can be said for baking. How did you find the gingerbread, Sam?"

"Well enough. To be truthful, a good meal is more my line. I get more than enough fancy fare at the big house."

He gave Annie his gentle smile and I sneaked away. As Alice had said, the rest was up to them. It did cross my mind, however, that food wasn't the only way to a fellow's heart – which proved that grown-ups didn't always get it right.

Anyway, the day ended well. Annie and Sam went off arm in arm for an evening stroll by the lake. Gyp scoffed down the piece of gingerbread I had saved him, and my friend Alice was delighted with the model of a treecreeper I had made her in my spare time.

So all in all, everyone was happy. ■

Tenby, Wales

THE picturesque harbour town of Tenby has long been a favourite with holidaymakers. It was the Victorians who first made Tenby a tourist hotspot and, with a mulititude of attractions on offer, it's just as popular today. *Dinbych y pysgod* is Tenby's Welsh name, meaning Little Fortress of the Fish.

Tenby Castle, which was built by the Normans in the 12th century, now has only a tower left standing, but the old town walls are among the most important surviving mediaeval city walls in Britain.

For those that like to explore an area on foot, Giltar Point is the start of the Pembrokeshire Coastal Path. Or you can hop aboard one of the cruises to nearby holy site Caldey Island, which is owned and run by Cistercian monks.

Tenby's narrow cobbled streets are home to an array of shops and you'll find a multitude of restaurants, pubs and coffee shops to dine in. ∎

Next Door's Cat

by Glenda Young

WHEN the kitchen door slammed shut, Karen turned to see Bill storming into the kitchen from the garden.

"That flaming cat!" he yelled.

Karen's heart sank.

"Oh, no, what's it done now?" she asked.

"Yes, Daddy, what's the naughty cat done?" Alison chimed in from the table where she was colouring in.

"Oh, it's nothing to worry about, sweetheart," Bill said, changing his tone swiftly as he spotted her. "The cat's just been walking over my seedlings again, that's all. Some of them got a bit squashed."

"Not again?" Karen said.

Bill walked over to her and whispered conspiratorially.

"And it's dug another big hole right in the middle of my veg patch."

Karen sighed. Bill and next-door's cat had been waging war against each other for months.

Bill loved spending time in their garden and looked on it as his special place.

So, it appeared, did the cat.

"I suppose we could have a look in the supermarket next time we're in there," Karen suggested. "We can see if they sell anything to keep cats away from the bits of the garden you don't want them messing with?"

Bill frowned.

"If I had my way, I'd shoot . . ."

"Bill!" Karen whispered, nodding towards Alison.

She watched with interest and amusement as Bill took a deep breath.

She knew he had to cover his tracks in case their daughter picked up on his anger and frustration with the furry feline from next door.

"I'd shoo them, that's what I'd do," Bill said brightly to Alison. "I'd shoo them right away."

Karen glanced at Alison and was relieved to see that she was deep in concentration over her colouring book again, not really paying any attention to her dad.

Karen and Bill watched as their daughter swapped a pink felt-tip pen for a brown one from her jar of pens.

"Shoo-shoo, cat, shoo-shoo," Alison sang to herself.

"What are you drawing, sweetheart?" Karen asked. The dining-room table had been covered in sheets of coloured paper and pens all morning while Alison worked away.

"It's Fluffy!" She smiled, holding up the picture.

"What's fluffy?" Karen asked, eyeing the picture, trying to work out what it was.

"Fluffy. He's the cat from next door," Alison said. "That's his name."

Karen and Bill exchanged a glance.

"How do you know it's called Fluffy?" Karen asked.

"I don't," Alison said. "I just made it up. That's what I would call him if he was mine.

Illustration by Sarah Holliday.

"I just gave the cat a name because Daddy doesn't like it and I feel sorry for it."

She turned the picture round to admire her handiwork.

"I like the cat, Daddy," she said. "Can we keep it?"

"No! We can't!" Bill said.

Karen smiled at Alison.

"What Daddy means is that the cat . . ."

"Fluffy?"

"Yes, what Daddy means is that we can't keep Fluffy because he's not our cat. Fluffy belongs to Mrs Gregson who lives next door."

Alison frowned.

"But if Fluffy belongs to Mrs Gregson, why does he keep coming into Daddy's garden?" she asked.

"That's what I'd like to know!" Bill muttered.

* * * *

Later that evening, when Alison was put to bed, she cajoled Karen into pinning her cat picture to the wall beside her night-light so that she could see

93

Fluffy as she fell asleep.

Karen joined Bill in the living-room, the two of them watching television companionably together while Alison slept upstairs.

"Promise me you won't do anything nasty to that cat, Bill," Karen said, only half joking. "Mrs Gregson would never forgive us if anything happened to it while it was over our side of the fence. She's had that cat for years.

"I remember when we first moved in she used to talk about the cat all the time. She'd be devastated if anything happened to it."

Bill picked up the remote control and started flicking up and down the channels.

"And I think Alison would be upset if anything happened to it, too," Karen added.

Bill smiled.

"Yes, she does seem rather taken by it, doesn't she? He is quite sweet, really – if he would just keep his rotten furry feet off my precious seedlings!"

"It might be time for Alison to have her first pet, you know," Karen said thoughtfully.

"I don't disagree," Bill said. "But when her first pet arrives, whatever it is, we're going to make quite sure that it's one that won't ruin my garden."

*   *   *   *

"Mummy, could I have some extra sandwiches today, please?" Alison asked the next day when Karen was preparing lunch.

"Are you hungry, love?"

"It's not for me, Mummy, it's for Fluffy. I've been feeding him."

Karen smiled at her daughter.

"Cats don't eat bread," she said. "They like fish and meat."

But Alison was adamant.

"Fluffy likes bread," she said. "He eats it all the time from my hands when I take the bread into the garden."

So that was why the cat had been hanging around in the garden over the last few months, Karen realised. If it had been getting fed, no wonder it was reluctant to leave.

But it was hard to say no to Alison's pleading gaze.

"Well, I'll tell you what we'll do," Karen said, raking around at the back of the cupboard for a tin of tuna.

"Let's see if the cat likes this instead. It'll be better for him than bread. Promise me you won't keep any more of your own food to give to the cat, Alison?"

The little girl nodded solemnly.

"I promise, Mummy."

"Good girl."

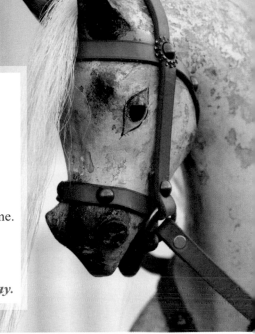

The Rocking Horse

MY birthday, three years old that day
And what a wonderful surprise –
A rocking horse, soft dapple-grey
With silver mane and long-lashed eyes!
He always had a starring role
In every carefree childhood game,
But years go by and children grow
And childhood games just aren't the same.
But then my children came along
And rediscovered my lost friend;
Their children, too, befriended him
And so his story has no end!

Eileen Hay.

Karen knocked the tuna from its tin into an old bowl. She took Alison by the hand, and the two of them left the kitchen and went into the back garden, expecting that the cat might be lurking around somewhere in need of some food.

Karen put the bowl on the ground and Alison called out for the cat but there was no sign of it anywhere.

Just when they were about to give in, leave the tuna outside and go back into the house, they heard a gentle mewling sound.

"It's the cat," Karen said. "It's here somewhere in the garden and it doesn't sound well."

There was no mistaking the noise of a crying cat and it didn't take long for Karen to find it hiding underneath one of the shrubs by the lawn.

As she walked towards it, she could see the cat licking a front paw over and over. As she got nearer still, Karen could see blood seeping from a wound in the paw.

"Oh, you poor thing," she cried. "What's wrong with you?"

While Alison stood and watched her, Karen knelt on the lawn and reached under the shrub with both hands for the cat, hoping it wouldn't take fright and try to scratch her or run away.

But it didn't try to move away and surrendered easily to Karen without any fight. She picked the cat up and cradled it gently, the wound on its poor paw clear to see.

"Come on, boy," she said. "Let's take you home."

With Alison trailing behind her, Karen walked with the cat in her arms to the house next door.

When Mrs Gregson opened her front door she was somewhat surprised by the scene that greeted her on her doorstep.

There was Karen with a cat in her arms, what looked like bloodstains on her T-shirt, and her young daughter standing beside her, looking extremely distressed.

"We found your cat in our garden," Karen said, holding it out to Mrs Gregson. "We heard it crying and I'm awfully sorry, but think it's got something wrong with its paw. Look, it's bleeding."

But Mrs Gregson made no move to take the cat from Karen's arms. Karen gently pushed the cat further towards her neighbour, wondering if she was a bit shocked.

"I think it needs to see the vet," Karen said firmly, but still Mrs Gregson didn't move.

She looked from Karen to the cat and back again.

"You're right," she said at last. "It does look as though it needs a vet's attention, and quick."

Karen moved again, positioning her body forward so that Mrs Gregson would have no choice but to take the cat from her. But Mrs Gregson took a step backwards into her hallway.

"It's no good giving it to me, love. That's not my cat," she said, shaking her head. "I can't take another cat in after Bobby passed away. He died last month. I had him for fifteen years, you know.

"He was a right good 'un and it broke my heart when he died. I was so upset that I promised myself I wouldn't have another one after Bobby had gone. At least, not for a good while."

Karen stepped back in shock. Meanwhile, the cat continued its mewling and snuffling in her arms.

"It's not yours?" Karen asked, confused. "Then whose is it? Where has it come from?"

"I've no idea, love," Mrs Gregson said. "It's probably a stray. There's enough of them round here.

"But if you ask me, you need to get it seen by a vet and as quick as you can. I used to take Bobby to the one on Newland Road."

Karen thanked her.

"Come on, Alison," she said as they walked back to their house. "Get a cardboard box and an old towel from the garage and then you can sit in the back of the car like a good girl with the box on your knee, and hold on to it tight."

"Are we going to make poor Fluffy well again, Mummy?" Alison asked with tears glistening in her eyes.

"I hope so," Karen said, mentally crossing her fingers.

* * * *

Karen tried not to recoil in shock when Stuart Brown, the vet, told her how much it would cost to treat the stray cat. But the poor little thing had to be taken care of, after all.

Then Stuart scanned the cat to see if it was microchipped, in which case there might be a chance it could be returned to its rightful owner.

But the scan showed no chip. The vet leafed through a book where the receptionist kept details of local cats reported missing.

Karen surprised herself by feeling more relieved than she expected when it looked like Fluffy wasn't on any missing list. She realised that she was growing attached to the little cat, and wanted to make sure it was well looked after.

She handed over the payment to the vet, wondering how on earth she was going to square things with Bill when she got home.

On the drive home in the car, Alison sat in the back of the car again, next to the box containing a sleeping cat with a bandaged front leg.

As Karen drove, she could hear Alison singing along to a tune again.

"Shoo-shoo, cat, shoo-shoo."

When the car stopped at traffic lights, Alison could see in the rear-view mirror the smile on Alison's face each time she glanced at the cat. In that instant, Karen knew what she had to do.

She knocked off the right turn indicator and flipped it to turn left instead. As soon as the lights turned green, she threaded her way through the streets and out on to the ring road that led to the out-of-town shopping park.

Leaving the cat sleeping in the box in the car, Alison and Karen headed into one of the big retail units. They took a trolley and filled it with tins of cat food and toys, a bed and a blanket.

Alison picked out a green collar with a special clasp where they could write their address and phone number, in case Fluffy ever got lost.

Karen then pushed the trolley across the vast store, heading to the gardening section, to the area that sold fencing, and selected some of the right size to protect a vegetable patch.

Bill wouldn't be home from work for hours and Karen knew she'd have plenty of time to get the fencing up and the cat settled in.

"I hope Daddy will be happy having Fluffy as our pet," Alison said a little doubtfully, as she helped Karen push the trolley. "I don't think he likes him very much, you know."

"Don't worry about your dad, love." Karen smiled. "You just leave him to me!" ■

iStock and Alamy.

Margarine

WHO would have thought that we first began swapping butter for margarine way back in 1869? It was Napoleon III of France who offered a prize to anyone who could produce a cheap butter substitute to sustain the army and his poorer subjects.

Chemist Hippolyte Mège-Mouriès found a way to churn beef tallow with milk to win the prize. His "oleomargarine" was patented in 1869, but commercial success had to wait until 1871 when a Dutch company bought his formula.

The new company realised that if it was to rival butter, margarine would have to look more like butter, and so yellow colouring was added for the first time. This was later banned in some countries because of objections from the dairy industry.

Even so, margarine began to sell in much greater quantities. The company that bought Mège-Mouriès idea later became part of Unilever, which manufactured some of the twentieth century's best-known brands such as Stork, Flora and I Can't Believe It's Not Butter.

A post-war shortage of beef fat led to new margarines based on vegetable oils, which are preferred today. Now Mège-Mouriès's original invention has inspired hundreds of dairy substitutes, including some suitable for vegans or with cholesterol-lowering properties for special diets. It's come a long way from helping Napoleon III to feed his army more economically! ∎

Illustration by Ruth Blair.

Playing With Fire

by Em Barnard

THE hippies appeared along the country lanes around Ann's home in the June of '67. They camped on scrubland let out by an aged farmer. Many of the older generation disapproved and made no secret of their feelings.

But to the kids and teenagers the hippies were stimulating and refreshing, far more exciting than the village hall disco. Many local youngsters made secret excursions to the camp, intrigued by their lifestyle, peaceful poems and music.

Ann had gone with a group of friends. There was something about the dreamy music that was mesmerising, and Ann became entranced by a guitarist called Ronnie.

He seemed quieter than the others, detached, the odd one out. But she and her friends kept a closed circle, never straying off alone, so she never got to speak to him.

And when the local bobby began strolling by, many, including Ann's group, decided it was safer to stay away.

Then Ronnie came to Ann's dad's farm to ask for a summer job. He was trim in a T-shirt and jeans, his dark hair curling round his ears. But the farmer shook his head, unsure of him.

The musician returned the following day. When he called the third day, Ann, closing the door on the hen run, picked up her basketful of eggs and went to her dad's side to see what was going on. Her younger brother Andy was already there, curious, too.

"I've worked on mixed farms before, sir," Ronnie was saying. "I'm a hard and honest worker. I could help bale and stack straw now the season's here again."

The farmer rubbed his chin thoughtfully.

"I'd have to employ you proper, mind."

"That's fine by me, sir." As the farmer thought on, Ronnie added, "I have my own caravan. If you could allow me a place to park it, I wouldn't need to return to the camp. I'm not really one of them – I was just hitching a lift, so to speak."

The farmer nodded.

"I'll give you a go, then. Come with me, and I'll take you to Bernie, our foreman."

"I'll take him, Dad."

"You get back to your chores, Andy." As the twelve-year-old sulked off he turned to Ronnie. "You'll get a lunch with the others in the yard. Do you smoke?"

"Yes, sir."

"I'll not have any of your funny fags here."

"I don't use them, sir."

"What's your name?"

"Ronnie Gillespie." He smiled and nodded at Ann as he walked by.

She headed indoors with a spring in her step.

"And what's put a smile on your face?" her mum asked.

"Dad's just taken that hippie on."

"Then heaven help us." Her mum pointed a warning finger at her daughter, and swung it to include her son as he ran in. "Just keep clear of him, both of you. If your father finds him anywhere near you, he'll get rid of him."

Ann knew it was true, but it didn't stop her looking. She'd had a couple of boyfriends, one a farm hand on another farm, but it had all been just a bit of fun.

Now there was a fluttering in her heart she'd never felt before regarding this quiet, methodical worker who kept to himself, and respected those around him.

Only the foreman Bernie took a dislike to him and would give him the meanest of jobs. Ronnie accepted them willingly.

✳   ✳   ✳   ✳

It was the last week in July and Ann, hand to her eyes against the sun, watched Ronnie hefting straw bales on a trailer and then jumping aboard to ram them tight.

He was working alone, ordered by Bernie to bale and stack the straw in the sheds close to the livestock pens. The other hands were over the ridge working on the larger fields, building the main stack.

Ann walked across the cropped field to him.

"I've brought your lunch. Didn't Bernie tell you to come into the yard with the others?"

"Job needs doing. It's going to rain. But I'll stop for five minutes." He jumped down and sat beside Ann against the rear tractor wheel. She lifted the tea towel from the basket. He reached for a cheese sandwich and a stick of celery.

She poured cider into an enamel mug and passed it to him.

"Dad's pleased with your work. He'd keep you on if you wanted."

When he just drained his mug and didn't answer, she was disappointed.

"So where's your home?"

He peered in the basket and selected another sandwich.

"Up north. What about you? You happy working on your dad's farm? No dreams to fulfil elsewhere?"

"Not really. Farming's in the blood for Andy and me. It's our inheritance, our future. A secure one, I hope. That's if Andy and I can work together. Nothing's straightforward where families are concerned, is it?"

It was a subtle way to glean further information. Ronnie gulped down his cider.

"I'm sure you and Andy will make a go of it. Thanks for the lunch. I'd best get on." He leaped to his feet.

"I could help."

He looked down on her from the trailer.

"No, Ann. You've got your own chores, and I don't want any trouble with your dad. Maybe you could make that clear to Andy." He nodded across the field.

The boy was racing towards them. Ann grabbed the basket and hurried to him.

"I came to help Ronnie," he said breathlessly.

"Dad'll get angry if you stop him working."

"But I want to show him the list of trains I spotted at the weekend."

"You can show him in the yard tomorrow. Come on." She grabbed his wrist and tugged him round.

The following lunchtime Ronnie was again in the field collecting the last of the bales, already crisping up in the heat after an overnight shower.

When Ann took his lunch, Andy was hefting bales on to the trailer, too. She was a bit miffed she had to share Ronnie, but soon they were groaning and giggling at Andy's daft jokes.

It was the first time she'd seen Ronnie relaxed and laughing. Her yearning for him increased.

* * * *

"Ann," her mum said a few weeks later. It was after lunch and she was sitting the washed plates in the grooved shelves of the Welsh dresser. "You like Ronnie, don't you?"

"Yes," Ann said, finishing off at the sink, watching Ronnie through the window as he walked from the yard with the other hands.

"He's asked your dad if he can stay on."

Ann swung round.

"Full time?"

She nodded.

"But your dad's unsure."

"Ronnie won't let him down."

"It's you he's unsure of. Your dad's not blind, Ann. He's noticed you and Andy hanging around Ronnie. But in your case, Ann, he worries it might turn to more than friendship."

"I can't help how I feel, Mum."

"I know, Ann," her dad answered, stepping through the back door. He went to the sink to wash his hands after an oily tractor repair. "We'll be one short when the young lad goes to agricultural college in a couple of weeks and that's my reason for considering Ronnie."

Ann passed her dad a towel.

"I have to talk to him – I can't avoid him. I've done nothing to be ashamed of."

He cupped her cheek with his damp hand.

"I know, Annie, love, but he isn't for you. He's had farming jobs before, but always moves on.

"He phones his mother from the box beside the pub Monday lunchtimes. His father's passed on.

"There's no law says he has to tell me personal details. But he seems content here, so we'll see."

"Great, Dad." Andy swung round the door. "I haven't done anything to be

The Rise And Fall Of A Tree

FROM a tiny tender seed
It grew and grew, until indeed,
No finer tree was in the wood,
No tree so tall had ever stood,
There for years and years and years,
Amongst the oaks and conifers,
Dressed in leaves of palest green,
To enhance the sylvan scene.
Then fate let a man arrive
With chainsaw, rope and four-wheel drive,
And quicker than it takes to tell
The proud and noble tall tree fell.
It took so many years to grow,
How sad it is to see it go,
To end cascading through the door,
As junk mail on the hallway floor!

Brian H. Gent.

ashamed of, either." He grinned at Ann as he came to the sink to wash his hands.

*   *   *   *

Later that day Ann caught up with Ronnie washing out the milking parlour.

"I hear you're staying on."

"Maybe."

Ann saw a frown on his face.

"You haven't changed your mind?"

He stopped to look at her.

"I've not been entirely honest with your dad. And if I were to speak to him . . . he might not want me to stay."

Ann swallowed, her heart racing.

"I'm sure you haven't done anything really bad. You haven't – been to prison, say?"

He gave an ironic laugh.

"You're not far out. You see, my parents had a farm. Dad died when I was thirteen. I still miss him.

"Our foreman said he'd help with the running of the farm till I was old enough to take charge.

"But he filtered stuff away, everything from hand tools to tractors. That's

iStock.

what got him caught. But the whole affair upset Mum – she thought he was working with us.

"We sold the farm and now Mum has a little house and works in a shop. She's happy, as long as I keep in touch."

"But Dad would understand all that."

"Would he, though? You see, when the foreman was caught he tried pushing the blame on me. And mud sticks.

"And the next thing I know I'm having trouble getting a job. So I hitched up our caravan and, well, here I am.

"I want to settle, stop running. Mum said I must tell your dad, and maybe she's right, because if I don't and Bernie finds out he'll have a field day and I'll be out on my ear."

Ann shook her head.

"Dad's never said anything against you. Whereas Bernie, well, he's just waiting for an excuse to get rid of him. But don't tell Dad yet, just in case.

"Just carry on, Ronnie, because Dad is really happy with your work. In fact, we all are, and we don't want you to leave." She set her hand on his bare forearm and smiled, hoping her affection for him shone through.

His return smile, however, showed in his face as anxious gratitude.

* * * *

Time has a way of easing the mind, especially when burdening factors are ousted. So when the hippie camp upped and towed away in early September, everyone was relieved.

Ann often walked the two dogs, off lead, along the lanes of the farm. Now she had a special route, passing the little field where Ronnie had parked his caravan.

If the dogs heard the gentle chords from Ronnie's guitar during the quiet autumn evenings, they'd dart off to him. Ann would follow, her heart swelling in delight.

Ronnie would smile warmly at her and then dip his eyes to the strings. But it was enough for Ann. Fearful she could be risking Ronnie his job if her dad found out, she never lingered.

* * * *

The seasons passed and all the farmhands, including Ronnie, moved on with them. Late July, and the main stack was again being built. It was dry, dusty work.

That day, the hands had been sent to their lunch. Bernie had stayed behind to watch Ronnie finish stacking the last trailer, twiddling with his cigarettes knowing Ronnie could do with a light-up, too.

In the yard, the men were finishing lunch when Andy was sent to find out what was holding back Bernie and Ronnie. Ann was helping her mum clear the table, her dad resting in his chair by the Aga.

Minutes later there was a commotion in the yard, raised voices, and suddenly Bernie slammed into the kitchen, Ronnie at his shoulder, both bleeding round the face and hands, hair and clothes prickled with straw and dust.

"I want him out!" Bernie snarled.

Her dad jumped up, waving the hustle of nosy men away from the door.

"What's happened?"

"The stack's on fire!"

The men were already through the gate, running.

The stack was a whooshing, crackling inferno, the heat scorching. They watched helplessly. A fire engine eventually arrived.

*   *   *   *

Later, after the men had washed down in the yard, finished work and gone home, Bernie and Ronnie were summoned to the kitchen.

"Well!" Her dad looked between them. "Which one of you was smoking?"

"Not me." Bernie shook his head.

"I didn't start it, sir," Ronnie answered calmly.

Her dad growled, infuriated.

"Is that your final answer?" Each remained mute. "Then you're both sacked. Get out!" As they left, he slumped down into his chair by the Aga, back to them all.

Ann watched as her mum put her hands on his slumped shoulders in comfort. Andy was standing, fists tight to his sides, not knowing what to do.

Ann did. She ran out and carried on running till she got to Ronnie's caravan. He was already hitching it to his old car.

"Ronnie! Don't go. I won't let you." She flung herself in his arms.

He tugged her from him, held her at arm's length.

"Ann, I love you and I've respected your father's wishes regarding you. I've worked hard. I've tried to prove to him I'm worthy of you, but it'll never work now."

"You love me?" Her face shone with joy.

Ronnie sighed heavily.

"Oh, Ann, I didn't mean to tell you, for it to end like this before it's even begun. You don't think I chose your farm randomly? Why do you think I've put up with Bernie and the fact he might find out about my past?"

Ann was unable to speak. She grabbed his arm.

"But you didn't start the fire; it was Bernie. He's trying to get rid of you, you know that."

"He's a good foreman, though he does have a nasty mouth. But I've never seen him light up other than in the yard. And we were fighting, remember?"

"But . . ." Ann tried to fathom it. "Take me with you."

Ronnie shook his head.

"You know that's not possible. Now go home, Ann." He pushed her gently from him, turned abruptly and reached into the car.

Ann watched him. Then she crept round the far side of the caravan, quietly opened the door and stepped inside.

*   *   *   *

Later that evening Ann stood on a hill and gazed across the patchwork downs in the direction of her home. A lone blackbird piped his fluting song, the trees calmly still as if fearing to intrude into her uneasy thoughts.

The fiery shades on the horizon were cast by the sun setting, but through Ann's tear-filled eyes, they quivered like real flames.

From behind, arms drew her into an embrace. Ronnie murmured in her ear.

"I'm sorry I shouted at you. But seeing you in there when I opened the door . . . Come on, time to go home. I'll stop at the first phone box and you can call your mum."

She turned and looked up at him.

"There has to be a way to prove Bernie started the fire."

He gently kissed her damp cheeks then led her to the passenger side of the car.

*   *   *   *

It was dark, past ten when Ronnie drew his caravan to a halt outside the farmhouse. The startling thing, when Ann stepped out of the car, was not her mum running out to clutch her in her arms, but her dad greeting Ronnie with a cordial nod.

"You'd best come in. There have been developments while you've been eloping with my daughter. We've found out who started the fire."

Ann gasped.

"Bernie's admitted it?" she asked.

"It wasn't Bernie." His eyes flashed to his son, sitting at the table, head dipped.

Andy swallowed.

"When I cleared the rise I saw Ronnie and Bernie at the stack, fighting. I ran on, but by the time I got there Bernie was running down the far side, Ronnie after him.

"Then I saw Bernie's cigarettes and matches on a bale. I put one between my lips to see how it felt. And then I struck a match. But I knew it was wrong, I did, Dad, I wasn't going to do it!

"But then the match stung my hand and I dropped it. And the flames scuttled off in all directions. I tried to stamp them out but they were faster than me."

Ann was shocked.

"I may owe you an apology," her dad said to Ronnie who, beside Ann, was staring at Andy, shocked, too. "But you owe me one for running off with my daughter."

Ann jumped in.

"No, Dad. I hid in the caravan. Ronnie didn't know till he stopped fifty miles up the road. He insisted on bringing me home." She raised her head and addressed her father defiantly.

"But I'll run after him again if he goes, because I love him, and he loves me."

The smile that passed between them proved it.

Her dad sat at the table opposite his son and looked at Ronnie.

"So what were you fighting over, you and Bernie?"

Ronnie cast an unwitting glance to Ann. Her dad nodded.

"Yes, I thought as much. His nasty mouth at work again. I won't be taking him back. But you can stay."

Delighted, Ann clutched Ronnie's arm. But Ronnie wasn't finished.

"I have to tell you things first, sir. You may not want to keep me on."

"I never take hands on full time without checking work references. I've also been in touch with your mother since last Christmas. Don't look surprised, she wrote to me first.

"Seems you . . . carelessly . . . put this address on the letter inside her card." He grinned. "She told me all about you and I promised I'd look after you. So you'd best stay on where I can do just that."

Ann jumped up in delight.

"Oh, Dad, thank you."

He stopped her with a wave of the hand.

"Just go, both of you. We'll talk later. I've another problem to settle first." He turned to his son.

Ann led a stunned Ronnie outside.

"See? It's turned out well after all," she said as they strolled to his car, lit by the glow of the porch light.

"Not for Andy."

"Oh, Dad'll walk him up over the ridge in the morning to check the scene of the crime. He'll give him a good talking to, and Andy will come back down a man."

"You've been watching too many films, Ann." Ronnie tugged her round the far side of the caravan into the shadows. "So you'll know how the films end, then?"

"Meanwhile, against a starry sky, the lovers kissed?"

No sooner were the words out of her mouth than his lips were pressing down on hers. ■

One Good Turn

by Toni Anders

T HE young woman on the doorstep smiled nervously as Celia opened the front door.

"Good evening," she said. "We don't know each other but I wonder whether you would let me come in and speak to you?"

"Why?" Celia asked.

"Because I want to apologise to you and discuss something."

"Apologise? I don't understand, and I'm not buying anything," she said firmly.

"I'm not selling anything." The girl gave a little laugh. "I'm a teacher at the school down the road, St John's Academy. My name is Janie Knight. I believe you had an – encounter – with some of our boys this morning."

"Cheeky little devils!" Celia's eyes flashed as she recalled the incident.

*   *   *   *

She had been looking over her gate, waiting for the postman as she often did on a sunny morning, when the small group of schoolboys came past.

They were fourteen or fifteen, old enough to treat people with respect, she thought.

One of them, shock-haired and freckled, finished a packet of crisps and tossed the bag over her hedge.

"Excuse me," she called. "Please don't throw rubbish into my garden."

He turned towards her, a sneer on his face.

"Call that a garden? Looks more like a jungle to me." Laughing raucously, he continued on his way.

Celia turned from the gate and began to walk slowly up the path. Tears welled up in her eyes as she surveyed the garden.

Gordon had been so proud of it. He'd worked on it every evening and visitors and tradesmen alike had always commented on the impressive, colourful display.

After he'd died, she'd done her best, weeding and watering and pushing the heavy mower across the lawn. But gradually it had become too much for her.

She'd enquired at the local post office about a gardener. Sayeed, the post master, had studied all the postcards offering services in the window, but there was no gardener.

"There is so much work for them nowadays, they don't need to advertise," he'd said. "But if I hear of anyone, I'll certainly let you know."

Celia discussed the problem with Mrs James next door.

"Even if you can find one, they charge fifteen pounds an hour," Mrs James told her.

"Fifteen pounds an hour?" Celia was horrified. "I couldn't afford that."

Illustration by iStock

Mrs James was lucky. She had a strapping young nephew who called in every so often and cut her lawn.

"Haven't you got anyone like my Rhys?" she asked. She knew Celia had no children.

"No, I'm afraid not." Celia turned sadly away.

* * * *

The young woman on the doorstep had one hand behind her back. She moved and held out a small bunch of freesias.

"This is an apology," she said. "I know one boy was very rude, but I'm afraid he has problems.

"The others are different. They told me what had happened. They're very sorry."

Celia took the flowers and held them to her face.

"My favourites," she admitted. "My husband, Gordon, used to grow them for me. Come along in. We'll have a cup of tea."

When Celia returned with the tea tray, Janie was gazing out of the window at the front garden.

"You said you wanted to discuss something." Celia poured tea into two cups.

"Every year," Janie began, "each class works on a project connected with the environment. We try to get the boys to see that with a bit of effort, they can make a difference to their neighbourhood. The best project gets a cup to hold for a year."

109

"Very good idea," Celia approved. "But I can't see that rude little monkey helping anyone."

"He's a difficult child," Janie agreed, "but he has his problems. There's no father and his mother is often ill. We are trying to change his attitude.

"And he's keen to take part in the project. He's very competitive and winning the cup appeals to him."

Celia sipped her tea thoughtfully.

"You've got your hands full there, I should think, but I wish you the best of luck. It sounds a very worthwhile idea. Now, where do I come in?"

Janie accepted another cup of tea and a cupcake.

"You're a very good cook," she said.

Celia smiled modestly.

"My hobby. I only wish I had someone to pass my skills on to."

"Please say if you don't like this idea," the girl said, "but I wondered whether you would let your garden be our project."

"My garden? My front garden?'

"Yes." Janie replaced her cup on the saucer and as she spoke, her face shone with animation. "We would make it over, cut the grass, remove old and dying plants and put new ones into the beds.

"It wouldn't cost you anything," she said hastily as Celia looked about to protest.

"We'd come on three Saturday mornings for two hours each week – if that would be convenient."

She sat back and gazed anxiously at Celia.

Celia looked towards the window. It was the answer to her prayers.

*   *   *   *

On Saturday morning, Janie and six young lads, all dressed for gardening, appeared on Celia's doorstep.

She looked at them in surprise, and realised she hadn't really believed they would come.

They'd brought their own forks and spades and shears and set to work at once.

"We've made a plan of what they'll do," Janie explained. "We'll cut the lawn, cut down all old growth and dig the flower-beds, then you can decide what you want us to plant."

Celia went back indoors. She picked up Gordon's photograph from its place on the piano.

"They're doing it for you," she whispered. "They'll make the garden the way you always had it, my darling."

Celia watched from the window as the work progressed. One boy, freckled and shock-haired, worked with great enthusiasm. It was the cheeky one who'd thrown rubbish into her garden.

He looked up and caught her watching him and for a moment they stared at each other, then he turned again to his work.

Celia went into the kitchen and began to lay glasses of lemonade and newly baked rock cakes on to a tray. She beckoned to Janie from the window.

The girl came into the kitchen.

"Elevenses," Celia announced. "I'm sure they're ready for something. They're working so hard."

The boys came in and washed their hands then sat in a row along the little wall at the end of the patio. They attacked the rock cakes with enthusiasm.

"My mum used to make these before she got ill," the freckled one said, taking another. "I love 'em."

"Why don't you make them for her?" Celia asked.

"Cooking? Nah, I couldn't do that."

After another half hour, they collected their belongings , changed their shoes and stood at the gate waiting for Janie.

Celia thanked them warmly.

"The garden looks better already. And you're coming again next week?" She found it hard to believe that anyone would be helping her for nothing.

That evening, she sat wondering what she could do to repay Janie, for it had been her idea.

Then she remembered the girl saying that the school was trying to change the cheeky boy's attitude to people. Perhaps she could help with that.

*　　*　　*　　*

The following Saturday the gardeners reappeared, seemingly as enthusiastic as before. This time they dug flower borders in preparation for the plants Celia would choose.

Janie had brought flower catalogues and while the boys drank their lemonade and demolished the plate of rock cakes, the two women settled down to choose flowers.

"I must have freesias, and I'd like the boys to choose some plants," Celia said. "It will remind me of them."

The boys grinned and shuffled their feet but looked pleased at the idea.

"You go first, Glenn," Janie said to the cheeky boy.

So his name is Glenn, Celia thought. Good. I can't keep thinking of him as the cheeky boy.

Glenn flipped through the catalogue.

"Them." He pointed to the photograph of small white flowers cascading over a wall. "I like them. They look – free.'

"I think I know what you mean," Celia agreed. "I like them, too. We used to call them snow-on-the-mountain."

When everyone had made a choice, Janie listed the plants and called the boys to get their tools together ready to leave.

"Last visit next Saturday,' she said. "We'll bring the plants and dig them in and hopefully all you'll need to do is a bit of watering."

"Do you know, I shall miss you all." Celia could feel tears welling up. "It's been such fun."

"And such a successful project," the young teacher said. "I'm sure we'll win the cup. I'll be calling in to take some more photographs, if that's all right with you. I'll let you have copies."

$$* \quad * \quad * \quad *$$

On the last Saturday everyone worked extra hard and soon the garden brimmed over with colour; blue delphiniums, red geraniums and yellow calendulas.

And spilling over a little wall in front of the window was Glenn's white snow-on-the-mountain.

Glenn came diffidently over to Celia as she sat admiring the garden.

"Um – I've enjoyed this," he said. "I'm sure we'll win the cup."

"I'm sure you will," Celia agreed. "It's a transformation."

"Could I . . . could I pop in now and then to keep an eye on the flowers – water them or pull up weeds?"

"Why, of course you can, Glenn. I should be glad of your help. But what can I do in return?"

Glenn looked at the ground.

"What I'd like . . ." he began. "Would you teach me to make rock cakes? Like you said, I could make them for my mum."

"Oh, Glenn, what a lovely idea. Of course I will. You come on Saturdays and we'll do some cooking then some gardening."

"You could be like my grandma, maybe," he said shyly. "I've never had a grandma."

Celia smiled warmly at him.

"I'd like that very much."

Janie came from behind a bush nearby from where she'd been listening to the conversation.

"There's been such a change in that boy lately," she said, taking a seat by Celia and watching Glenn walk away, " and it's all thanks to you and your garden."

"If you win the cup, we'll all have our desires," the older woman said.

"I've heard on the grapevine at school that we're almost certain to win," Janie said happily.

"And now I'm going to be a grandma for the first time!" Celia took Janie's hands in hers. "What a lovely summer this is going to be." ■

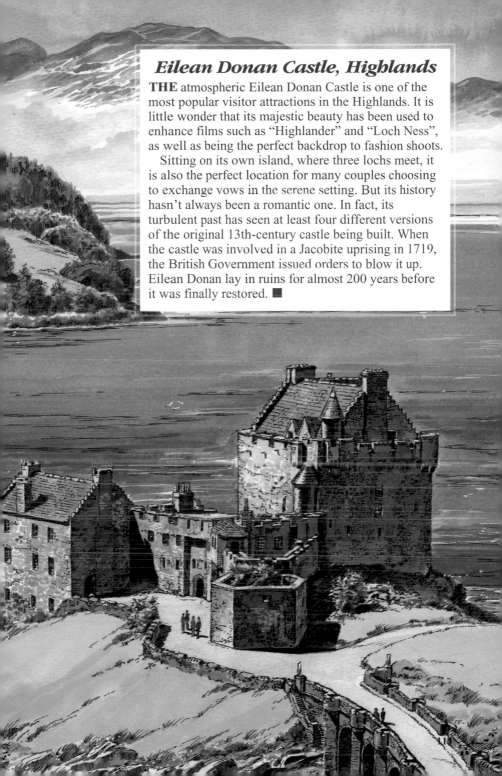

Eilean Donan Castle, Highlands

THE atmospheric Eilean Donan Castle is one of the most popular visitor attractions in the Highlands. It is little wonder that its majestic beauty has been used to enhance films such as "Highlander" and "Loch Ness", as well as being the perfect backdrop to fashion shoots.

Sitting on its own island, where three lochs meet, it is also the perfect location for many couples choosing to exchange vows in the serene setting. But its history hasn't always been a romantic one. In fact, its turbulent past has seen at least four different versions of the original 13th-century castle being built. When the castle was involved in a Jacobite uprising in 1719, the British Government issued orders to blow it up. Eilean Donan lay in ruins for almost 200 years before it was finally restored. ∎

The Last Bus

by Susan Sarapuk

WELL, this is it, then."

Judy looked up as Clare Randall got on the bus.

"The last bus from Roseby Layton. It's criminal." She sat down in the seat in front of Judy. "All those protests came to nothing. They just weren't prepared to listen to what we had to say. There's always been a bus service out of the village. Can you believe it?"

She wasn't the only one grumbling this morning; all the regulars had got on with long faces. The company was withdrawing the number 46 service as there weren't enough passengers to make the route profitable.

That certainly wasn't the case today. Judy had never seen so many passengers on the 7.40 into town, but it was too little, too late – nothing could be done now to save it.

Many people felt nostalgic about the bus route. Her own mother said it held fond memories.

"I met your father on the number forty-six," she often reminisced. "I was on my way into town to my job at the coffee bar; his motorcycle had broken down so he had to catch the bus into work that day.

"The seat next to mine was the last one available so he sat down and we started chatting. By the end of the journey we'd arranged to go on a date and the rest is history."

Many people would have said that meeting your partner on a bus was the stuff of romcoms and soap operas, but it had actually happened to her parents, so it really did work out that way for some people. Fat chance of it happening to her, though.

Judy knew all the regulars – Mr Evans, the elderly gentleman with a large moustache and tweed jacket and briefcase who went into the library every day, the two blonde women with painted nails and red lipstick who worked in the hair salon, and the sullen young man with trousers around his thighs and pulled-down baseball cap.

Then there was Mrs Lacey, the plump, middle-aged woman who stopped off in town to do some food shopping before going on to visit her elderly father, and Clare who worked in the farm shop on the outskirts.

They were all there today, as usual, augmented by nostalgia hunters who were all talking about what a pity it was that the service was being discontinued.

114

Illustration by Sarah Holliday.

If only they'd all used it more often then it wouldn't have been withdrawn, Judy thought.

She had a car which she could drive into work from now on, but she'd always used the bus because she wanted to support the service, and sometimes it was just nice to let someone else take the strain while she looked out of the window or caught up with everyone's news.

It wasn't going to be the end of the world for her, but what was someone like Mrs Lacey going to do from now on?

Judy stared out of the window and watched the frothy hawthorn hedges pass by. She'd made this journey every weekday for the past three years, but this was to be the last time.

Life was full of changes, even when you didn't want them, and sometimes you just had to adapt.

* * * *

Darren had wanted her to leave Roseby Layton.

"There's a big wide world out there – why wouldn't you want to explore it?" he'd said.

"I know there is. I studied and trained in London, remember."

"Don't you want to go back?" Darren demanded. "That's where the buzz is. That's where stuff is going on."

But Judy had always felt a deep connection to the hills of home. They'd always drawn her back. As soon as she'd got established as a solicitor she'd moved back to Roseby Layton from London.

It was her home and she didn't want to be anywhere else. Oh, she didn't mind travelling if Darren wanted to travel – two weeks at a time was fine, and going away made her appreciate what she had at home even more – but she was adamant that she was not going to relocate.

That had been when she'd begun to wonder if she and Darren would stay together.

He was not a Roseby Layton man even though he'd moved there to work at a small design studio on the edge of the village.

She'd met him through Ken and Iris who ran the business and had thought the two of them would hit it off, so had introduced them.

Darren had moved up from a job in London fancying a quieter country life, and for a while they'd clicked, taking long walks on the weekends so she could show him her world, eating pub lunches on a Sunday, playing board games in the evenings and watching box sets together.

She'd thought he was perfect, that he shared her dream, but the cracks had begun to show.

Judy had been at his flat over the studio one night when he'd suddenly said, "It's very parochial here, you know, Jude. I've enjoyed it but I don't think it's where I want to be in the long term. I think it's time to get back to the city, actually.

"And you could get a high-flying job in London. There are so many opportunities; you could treble your earnings."

"But I don't want to go back to London," Judy said, dismayed. "This is where I belong."

"OK." He'd shrugged and the topic had been dropped, but she knew it was not forgotten.

Judy spoke to her mother about it.

"If you end up being the one to do all the compromising then it's not love," she cautioned her daughter.

"That's all right for you to say, Mum." Judy had sighed. "You met Dad on the number forty-six. How likely is it that I'll meet someone around here?"

Then Darren had dropped the bombshell. He'd already got another job in London. He'd been to the interview and accepted the offer without telling her about it.

"I'm going, Judy," he said, and she could tell by the tone of his voice and the determined tilt of his chin that he meant it. "But you can come with me."

She shook her head.

"I can't. I really can't."

When it came right down to it there had been no doubting the decision, but three months on it still hurt and there were occasions when she really missed him.

* * * *

Judy sighed. Sometimes life was full of changes which sometimes you didn't want, even if they were for the better. You had to stop looking behind and press on to the next thing.

She knew she wouldn't have traded this in for the bright lights of London. This was where her heart was. At least she got to know her clients on a personal level, and life wasn't just about money.

She turned round to Mrs Lacey in the seat behind her.

"How are you going to manage to get into town from now on?"

"Oh, I suppose I'll get a taxi."

Judy frowned.

"Three times a week? That would be expensive. I'll be driving in every weekday from now on so I could give you a lift, if you like."

"Really? That would be so kind of you." Mrs Lacey looked relieved and Judy was glad she'd suggested it.

"I'll pick you up at the bus stop in the morning. What about you, Mr Evans?" she said to the old man across the aisle.

"I'll be fine, young lady. My son will collect me." He tipped his hat to her.

Judy felt a warm glow inside. It was nice to belong to a community and to help each other out.

"What happened to that young man you were seeing?" Mrs Lacey suddenly said, extinguishing the warm glow.

"Oh." Judy paused. "He went back to London." She decided to be honest. "And I didn't want to go with him."

"Don't you worry, love, he wasn't right for you. You're a good girl and someone will come along one day. Didn't your mother meet your father on the number forty-six?"

"I think that story's sunk into local folklore." Judy chuckled. "A pity it will be forgotten after today when the bus service stops."

The bus was stopping at the crossroads. Judy looked up as a young man climbed aboard.

He was dressed in hiking clothes and had a rucksack on his back, and Judy particularly noticed the way his dark hair fell into his eyes as he bent his head to count out his money.

Something inside her did a somersault and she felt herself colouring. Her heart began to race as he walked up the aisle looking for a seat.

There was only one spot left – next to her. Judy shifted over and he swung his rucksack off his back before sitting down.

"Thanks," he said, and as their eyes connected she felt as if she knew him, and his eyes seemed to be saying the same.

"I've just moved into a cottage down the lane. I'm glad there's a bus service."

"Not for long, love." Clare turned round in the seat in front. "It's the last bus. They're stopping the service tomorrow."

"Oh, rats, that's bad timing," he said. "I'm starting a new job in town tomorrow and I don't know my way around yet.

"I thought I'd get out and see some of the countryside today. Well, maybe I'll buy a bicycle."

Mrs Lacey tapped him on the shoulder.

"This young lady here will be driving in tomorrow morning. I'm sure she could squeeze you in."

Judy went bright red.

"It's all right, love, I'll be in the car with you. What can he do if we're both there?"

The stranger coloured as well. They both looked at each other, not sure what to make of Mrs Lacey's forwardness, then laughed.

"Actually, I'd be happy to give you a lift, if you like. At least that way you'll get to know a couple of people," Judy said. "Where did you stay before you came here?"

"Oh, that would be great, thanks," he said. "I've just moved up from London. I couldn't wait to get out of the city. I think I'm a country boy at heart."

*   *   *   *

"I really think there should be a commemorative plaque at this bus stop," Judy said as she and Paul sheltered from the sudden shower in the redundant bus shelter.

It had been six months since the last bus had run past there, although the old timetable was still on display.

"It's quite clearly the most romantic bus route in Yorkshire. That needs to be recognised!"

"And it's the luckiest, as well," Paul agreed. "I reckon they should open a lottery booth here. The odds are bound to be better than buying a ticket in some boring supermarket."

"It turns out you really can meet the love of your life on the bus. But who would have thought it would happen to two women in the same family?" Judy leaned in to him and he squeezed her.

"I'm so glad I caught the last bus." He kissed the top of her head.

Life was full of changes. But sometimes they happened for the better. ■

PERIODIC TABLE OF THE ELEMENTS

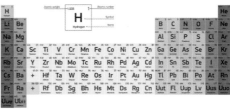

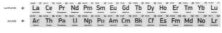

The Periodic Table Of The Elements

FROM the earliest days, scientists have tried to discover more about the building blocks that make up the world around us. The Ancient Greeks came up with the idea of the atom, which they thought was the smallest possible particle of the pure elements that made up everything else.

Later scientists discovered the properties of some of the elements, but didn't have a way to predict the properties of elements they suspected to exist, but hadn't yet found. In 1869, a Russian chemist, Dmitri Mendeleev, changed all that.

Writing down the properties of the elements on cards and playing with them as if in a game of Patience, Mendeleev realised that there were repeating patterns amongst the 70 known elements when he put them in order of increasing atomic weight.

After some rearranging, he arrived at the familiar vertical columns and rows we see today. His brilliant insight was to leave gaps for elements that were not yet known. Within 15 years, three of those elements had been discovered (gallium, scandium and germanium) – and they possessed the chemical properties Mendeleev had predicted and fitted precisely into the relevant gaps in his table.

Mendeleev died in 1907, having achieved international recognition. In 1955, when element 101 was discovered, it was named Mendelevium in honour of his achievement, which still forms the basis of the modern periodic table. ■

iStock and Alamy.

To The Rescue

by Rebecca Mansell

WHAT a day!" Rita took a quick sip of her coffee and then made a face. "Ouch, that's hot."

"Well, it did come from a boiled kettle." Susan smiled at her friend. "Perhaps you should be drinking chamomile tea instead of coffee?"

"I know, I do need to calm down," Rita said. "I just find it difficult to cope with John. Out of all the members . . ."

"He's the most trying?" Susan finished for her. "I just think he feels as if he has something to prove."

"Yet he fought in the Korean war." Rita grimaced. "How many times must we hear the tales?"

Susan chuckled.

"He is a very brave man, though. He only just managed to escape capture . . ."

"Surprised he wasn't awarded the Victoria Cross," Rita put in with a disgruntled expression.

"Now, now." Susan wagged a finger at her friend. "He does have the medals to show his courage. Not that I've seen them as yet."

Rita sighed heavily.

"He may well do, but when we set up 'Friends Are Us', our main aim was to bring together older people who had found themselves isolated in the community. The idea was to share common interests like music, reading, movies and light-hearted discussions. To look forward . . ." Her voice drifted off.

Susan nodded with concern.

"I know, and you're worried that John is obsessed with the past. But Rita, we have never asked a member to leave."

Rita took a sip of her now cool coffee.

"Well, if only we could find a way to involve him in the group's activities, I think the general mood would lift."

Susan looked down at her paperwork and smiled.

"Ellen Lawson is coming today. Do you remember me mentioning her dropping in that day when you had to take care of your little grandson? She's such a lovely lady, and very talented, too.

"She can play the piano and sing. She was quite famous in her day, apparently. Maybe she'll be a peaceful influence on him."

Rita looked at Susan dubiously.

"If she manages to distract John Walker, I'll buy you a lemon meringue tart every week for a month!"

Susan laughed.

"You're on!"

As Rita turned to leave the office, she glanced over her shoulder.

"And if I win, and John continues to regale us all with war tales, you can buy me a box of that chamomile tea. Better make it ten boxes!"

*　　*　　*　　*

Illustration by Pat Gregory.

When Ellen Lawson arrived at the village hall, it caused a bit of a stir.

"She's beautiful, isn't she?" Rita whispered to Susan. "Very elegant. I can see now why she was famous years ago."

Susan chuckled softly.

"Just look at Edward and Jim. I think it's love at first sight for them!"

The two friends watched with amusement as the gentlemen fell over themselves to welcome Ellen to their group. She just smiled at them shyly.

Only John stood back, observing silently.

"She seems quite happy," Rita said thoughtfully. "But didn't you say she's lonely?"

Susan nodded.

"I'm afraid she doesn't have any family left. Her only daughter died as a child. No other living relatives."

Ellen turned to look at them at that moment and smiled.

"We must introduce ourselves," Rita said, beaming back. "And show her the piano . . ."

"Did I hear the word 'piano'?"

Ellen's voice was soft but melodious as she strolled towards them, her head held high. She walked like a model. Rita and Susan shared a quick look.

"Yes, we do have one. It's a bit old and may need a little tuning . . ." Susan began.

"Oh, that will be fine." The older lady laughed. "Sounds a bit like me."

Rita giggled and Susan shook her head, smiling.

"Would you like a cup of tea?" she asked.

"Oh, yes, please. There is such a lovely atmosphere here. Everyone seems so nice."

Ellen glanced around at the admiring members of the friendship group.

Then John caught her eye.

"Does he always stand like that?" she said very quietly to Susan. "Like a soldier, waiting for battle to commence?"

Susan smiled awkwardly.

"I'm sure John will have many tales to tell you once he gets to know you."

"I'll look forward to that," Ellen said as she followed them. "I do hope he appreciates music."

"So do I," Rita muttered under her breath.

*   *   *   *

On the following Monday, the day the group always met, the sun shone outside the hall and inside.

It was all because of Ellen.

She held everyone spellbound with her piano playing. She could play classical pieces and modern tunes. She even took requests.

A few members had tried to play the old piano before but this was like listening to true talent.

Before Susan and Rita knew it, everyone was dancing and laughing.

John was the only one who didn't join in. He simply sat at the side, gazing at Ellen.

"I'm not sure if he's enjoying the music or not," Rita whispered.

"He is tapping his foot," Susan observed.

Suddenly Ellen stopped playing and got up from her seat. She winked at Rita and Susan and approached John.

Ellen spoke to John very quietly and then he obediently followed her back to the piano.

She began to play again but this time, John turned the pages of the music book for her.

"He's smiling, look!" Rita said.

"So he is!" Susan laughed with delight. "I think this could be the sign of new times for our group."

*   *   *   *

Little did Susan or Rita realise just how true Susan's words were to become.

A gentle but warm relationship began to grow between two members of the friendship group as the weeks progressed – Ellen and John.

It was quite a surprise.

122

"Well," Susan said reasonably, "there isn't anything in our made-up rule book to say that members can't have a relationship."

Rita smiled.

"They were holding hands walking into the group this morning."

"Well, let's make sure we don't place them in the back row later when we put on the film."

"Has John's request come up, then, for the movie tonight?"

Susan nodded.

"Yes. 'The Guns Of Navarone'."

"I hope Ellen doesn't get bored."

"Well." Susan looked thoughtful. "I think Ellen and John have a lot in common, John being the war hero that he is, and Ellen's first husband having died in the Korean war, the same war he talks about so much."

"Oh, so maybe she doesn't mind his battle stories, after all." Rita's eyes twinkled. "Her first husband? Has she been married many times?"

"Think how many cups of coffee you've had today," Susan replied.

"Three," Rita answered without thinking and then her eyes widened. "Really? Mind you, you did say she was famous once. Bit like Elizabeth Taylor!"

Susan chuckled.

"If this romance continues, maybe John will become husband number four!"

*   *   *   *

"Did that really happen?"

Rita's expression was ashen as she nursed her mug of coffee.

"It did," Susan replied sombrely.

"I am still in shock." Rita shook her head.

They fell silent as they remembered the previous week.

It had all begun so well . . .

*   *   *   *

"OK, everyone, take your seats, the movie is about to begin!" Susan called out cheerily as Rita organised the members so that they all could see the large television screen.

John and Ellen sat at the back, holding hands and occasionally gazing at each other affectionately.

It was about the middle of the film that Susan and Rita noticed that there was something wrong with John.

Ellen was trying her very best to comfort him but suddenly he stood up.

"Pause the film," Susan hissed to Rita.

Rita did so as John moved to the front of the room and looked anxiously at his fellow members.

"I have something important to say. Watching that film, sitting with Ellen – it made me think . . ."

"What is it, John?" Jim asked.

There was a pause and Susan and Rita watched John compose himself.

"I have been lying."

Everyone looked at each other in confusion.

John cleared his throat.

"I haven't been telling the truth. I don't have any medals. I am not a war hero. I made it all up."

There was silence as everyone stared at him. Susan and Rita exchanged looks.

Then the members began to talk quietly to one another, casting furtive glances at John.

"But why?" Ellen's gentle voice asked from the back. "Why, John?"

"I was a cook, that's all. Just a cook, in the Army," he replied, surveying his fellow members with tears in his eyes. "And I just thought I didn't matter. How important is a cook? I wasn't a soldier. I didn't save lives."

Everyone fell silent again at this confession, but it was suddenly broken by John.

"I'm so sorry." And he rushed out of the room, leaving a stunned audience behind.

While Rita tried to calm everyone down, Susan went after John, but he had disappeared.

John Walker had told the truth and that could only mean one thing – he didn't matter to anyone. Not to the members of the friendship group he had joined because he had always been so lonely since the war, or his new love Ellen.

He was still the cook that didn't matter . . .

"Ellen has asked me if she could say something to the members after lunch today," Susan said to Rita in the office.

"Must be about John."

"I just hope he turns up today, after his confession." Susan frowned.

"Oh, he will."

"How do you know that?" Susan looked at her friend with surprise.

"Well . . ." Rita smiled enigmatically. "I've always prided myself on being a little intuitive, perhaps psychic. So I predict he will be here today."

"Or he'll attend because he is in love with Ellen?"

*   *   *   *

Rita was right, and John did turn up.

Lunch was very quiet until Ellen got up and went to the front to face everyone.

"I'm glad you are all here as I have something I want to share with you," she said. She certainly had a way of mesmerising her audience. Then she began to read from a single piece of paper that she held.

"It's not easy here, my darling Ellen, but you really mustn't worry about me. We still find ways to feel happy. Thomas tells very good jokes that make us chuckle and David sings songs to us to raise our morale. He has a very pleasant voice.

"He may not be as harmonious as you (and I do so miss your singing) but we clap along. We also play cards and talk of our families waiting for us at home. That keeps us going.

"But do you know what really reminds me of home? The steak and kidney pie that Cook makes! It's so delicious. We can actually ask him what we would like to eat (within reason) and he makes it.

"John Walker really is the most marvellous cook. I don't know what we would do without him. At the end of the day, he sustains us, not just with his food but his stories, too. He has such an imagination. So, dear Ellen, I still look forward to each day.

"But of course, what I look forward to most, is coming home to you."

Ellen finished the letter with tears in her eyes.

"My husband died in the Korean war, but I have kept all his letters and they comfort me. I know that, despite everything, he was happy."

The members swivelled round in their seats to look at John.

"John, you were the cook!" Jim exclaimed.

"He was indeed," Ellen said. "Last night, I sought comfort in my husband's letters and, well . . . John, please come here."

Susan and Rita watched in amazement as John Walker moved towards Ellen, his head held high. He was a very different man from the one that had rushed out of the room the day before.

Once he reached Ellen, she stood on her tiptoes, kissed his cheek and whispered, "Thank you," in his ear.

Then she turned to face her enraptured audience.

"Let's give a big hand to John Walker – the cook that mattered!"

As the members of "Friends Are Us" clapped with gusto, she turned, smiling, to John.

"You think you didn't save lives but you did something extra – you saved those soldiers' spirits. You were very important."

And as John smiled proudly at everyone in front of him, Rita leaned over to Susan.

"I love steak and kidney pie. Do you think he might be able to help out next time for lunch?"

Susan beamed back.

"Only if he can make lemon meringue tart, too!" ■

The Cake Lady

by Gail Crane

SEVEN YEAR-OLD Cora gazed at all the delicious-looking cakes on display and just knew her grandpa didn't stand a chance – again. This was the second year she had come with him to the village flower and produce show, and the second year he had entered the cake section.

Cora thought her grandpa was the best and cleverest grandpa in the whole world. There was hardly anything he couldn't do, from building her a tree house in the big oak that grew outside her bedroom window to mending her daddy's car when it broke down; which was often because her daddy was a writer and, according to her mummy, he lived in another world.

Cora wasn't sure where that world was, but she did know it meant Daddy sometimes forgot to do things he was supposed to do and so Grandpa did them instead.

There was only one thing Grandpa couldn't do, and that was bake a cake.

Cora remembered Granny making cakes. She remembered sitting in the cosy kitchen with the smell of fresh baking coming from the oven and then sometimes, as a special treat, being allowed to have a slice of warm cake straight from the oven. Granny had always entered her cakes in the village show and she always won prizes.

But Granny was in another world now, though apparently not the same one as Daddy, so Grandpa had to make his own cakes and, last year, just like Granny, he had entered one in the village show. He hadn't won anything, though.

"Better luck next year, eh, Cora?" he'd said. But Cora knew it would take more than luck for her grandpa to bake a winning cake.

This year he had entered again.

"Reckon we've got a winner this time, love?" he'd said with a grin.

Cora didn't think so but she was determined to do something about it. She had a plan and, if it worked, maybe next year would be different. And she knew just the person to help her achieve it.

$$* \quad * \quad * \quad *$$

Geoff hated to admit defeat. He was an optimist and believed it was possible to do anything if you just tried hard enough, but he'd been trying hard for two years now and even he was beginning to think this was one thing that might be

Illustration by Mandy Dixon.

beyond him.

Grace had made such wonderful cakes. Some of his happiest memories were of her and Cora together in the kitchen, discussing what cakes they would make for that year's show, and of Cora's expression of delight as she tasted the results of the practice runs.

He had always been proud of how well Grace did, one year even winning the cup for the best in show, and when she died he'd decided to carry on the tradition himself.

In a funny sort of way, doing something she had loved so much made him feel close to her.

He'd never made a cake in his life but it couldn't be that difficult, could it? You just found a recipe and followed the instructions.

He never expected to do as well as Grace had, of course, but he believed it was all about making the effort. So he did.

And he'd told himself that this would be the year he won something, even if it was only a reserve.

This time he was entering rock cakes. He reckoned if the results of his attempts at a Victoria sponge and a Madeira cake were anything to go by, he should be able to turn out a pretty commendable rock cake.

They'd certainly looked fairly rocky when they came out of the oven. Some had spread a bit further than others so they were all different sizes, and quite a few of the currants were rather charred so he'd pulled them out.

As soon as they were cool enough, he'd bitten into one to try. Well, it had tasted good, but he did have a sneaking feeling that perhaps it was a little rockier than it was supposed to be.

Clearly the judge agreed with him.

Mrs Harman had smiled and said how good it was to see another man competing in the baking section, but he noticed that she seemed to have some difficulty breaking off a sample to test and, perhaps wisely, refrained from actually tasting it.

He decided to buy a cup of Mrs Perkins's builder's tea to cheer himself up.

"Ice-cream, love?" he asked Cora.

Cora smiled and shook her head, saying she wanted to stay to watch the judging.

*   *   *   *

Margaret was not having a good day.

First she'd mislaid her large cake tin and wasted half an hour searching for it before remembering she had lent it to her sister, Pauline, who had clearly forgotten to return it.

Luckily her sister lived only a few streets away so Margaret decided she just had time to cycle round to collect it and still be in time for the show. Foolishly, she'd ignored the ominous clicking coming from the pedals.

Back home again, she'd loaded her cakes into tins and, with efficiency born of several years of taking cakes to the village show, stacked the tins into her cycle baskets.

The trip to her sister had made her late; otherwise, she might have taken more notice of that click. She really must get it seen to, but for now she needed her bike to get to and from the village hall.

She also needed it to get to the school where she taught evening classes.

She had been a school teacher all her life. Her subject used to be called domestic science, later it became home economics, but always it involved cooking.

Teaching was her passion. So much so, she had let it take over her life and it was only when she reached sixty she realised how all-consuming her career had become.

Suddenly she found herself alone and single with nothing to fill her days, and close as she was to her sister and her family, that didn't fill the vacuum retirement had created.

Child Of Mine

I WOULDN'T change a hair
Upon that downy little head,
Or anything upon your face
That's crumpled up and red.
Not a single tiny eyebrow
Nor a single eye lash curl,
Not a single fisted finger
With its tiny nail of pearl.
I wouldn't change those eyes
That have the whole wide world to see,
For precious newborn child of mine,
You are the world to me.

Linda Brown.

She no longer felt needed. How she wished she could find something that would make her feel useful again.

Then her sister had found the ad in the local paper.

"There's a new programme of evening classes for adults starting in September," Pauline had told her, "and they're still looking for someone to teach cookery. It'd be right up your street."

It was just what she needed. Eagerly, she'd applied and, to her amazement, got the job.

Then one day she made a wedding cake for one of her students which led to a request for an eighteenth birthday cake.

Margaret entered competitions, baked for the WI market and the village fayres and found that her reputation grew steadily. She became known as the cake lady.

Her life was busier than ever – so busy, she sometimes let other things slide, things like having her bike serviced.

Part way to the village hall, bike and chain finally parted company. With a groan of frustration, she wheeled the bike the rest of the way and was only just in time to lay out her entries before the judging began.

iStock.

She was soon drawn in to the friendly chatter of her fellow exhibitors and, cheered by her two first-place rosettes and one second, what was left of the afternoon passed quickly.

It was only as she packed her cakes away that she thought of the long walk home.

*   *   *   *

"Are you the cake lady?"

Margaret looked down at the little girl and chuckled.

"Yes, I suppose I am," she said, "and who are you?"

"I'm Cora," Cora replied. "Can you teach my grandpa how to make a cake?"

"Your grandpa?" The child seemed familiar but Margaret couldn't quite place her. "Well, yes." She reached in her bag and pulled out a leaflet. "Why don't you give him this and he can come to one of my lessons. We do baking on Thursday evenings."

Cora shook her head.

"He won't come. He says he's 'not going to make an exhibition of himself in front of a group of women'."

Margaret couldn't help smiling.

"Couldn't you, please, go to his house?" Cora continued. "I can pay you," she added. "I've got three pounds and fourteen pence saved in my piggy bank."

"Oh, I don't think . . ."

"You see," Cora said quickly, "Granny always won prizes with her cakes but she's not here any more and Grandpa says he's remembering her by entering his cakes but he's hopeless at baking and so I thought if someone would just show him what to do he might win something."

Ah, that was where she had seen Cora before. Of course, she had come to the shows with Grace.

"I thought you looked familiar," she said. "Your granny was Grace Farmer, wasn't she? And so your grandpa must be Geoff."

Cora nodded.

"Yes. And those are Grandpa's cakes." She pointed to the rock cakes.

"Oh, dear. He certainly could do with a little help, couldn't he? Look, I'll tell you what, because I knew your granny, I'll see what I can do and I just might have an idea.

"Where is your grandpa now? I'm surprised I haven't seen him around already."

Cora pointed.

"He went to get a cup of tea. He said he didn't want to wait for the judging."

Margaret smiled kindly at the little girl.

"Well, I'll have a little chat with him when he comes back. Just you leave it

130

with me."

Margaret remembered how Grace used to say how lucky she was to have such a handy husband; how there was nothing he couldn't turn his hand to. Perhaps she could use that to persuade him.

Grace had been good to her when she first started coming to the village shows, making her feel welcome and introducing her to other villagers. It would be good to be able to do something in return.

* * * *

"Margaret! How nice to see you."

"You, too, Geoff. It seems a long time. Though I'm afraid I have to confess an ulterior motive. I have a favour to ask of you."

Geoff was surprised when Grace's old friend approached him but he was only too happy to help her.

"Of course I can look at your bike," he agreed. It was just the sort of thing he loved to do. "I'll need my tools, so let's go back to my place."

They loaded her cakes into the bike's baskets and, with Margaret and Cora carrying his own tins, he wheeled the bike back to his house. They carried everything into the kitchen.

"Why don't you stay and have a cup of tea with Cora, Margaret, while I fix the chain?" Geoff invited her. It was a long time since he had entertained anyone and he was enjoying having company.

"Thank you. I'd like that."

"I'd offer you a rock cake but I'm not sure it would be a good idea." Margaret smiled.

"A little, um, rocky, are they?"

"I'm afraid so. You see, I just don't know what I'm doing wrong. It all looked so easy when Grace made cakes."

"Cooking takes practice, Geoff, and knowing the right way to do things. I could teach you, if you like?"

He shook his head. Cora had already suggested cookery lessons, but he was having none of that.

"No, thank you, I'm not going to any classes."

"You don't need to. If you like, I could come here. It will be a fair exchange. You mend my bike and maybe give it a bit of an overhaul and I'll show you how to make cakes."

Cora jumped up excitedly.

"Say yes, Grandpa. Please say yes."

Geoff looked at his granddaughter and then at Margaret. There was definitely something going on here.

"What have you two been plotting?"

Margaret raised her eyebrows.

"Plotting? I don't know what you mean."

"Nothing, Grandpa, honest," Cora declared, trying unsuccessfully to look innocent.

Then they all burst out laughing.

"OK," Geoff said. "I give in. I think that's a lovely idea, Margaret. Thank you. But only on condition you let me do some jobs for you. I might not be able to bake a cake but I'm pretty handy with most other things."

Margaret held out her hand.

"Agreed."

"Good. Now, you have that cup of tea and I'll go and mend this bike."

As he went out of the door, he saw Cora and Margaret give each other a thumbs-up. He chuckled. Margaret was nice.

He would enjoy talking to someone who knew Grace, and he suddenly found himself looking forward to the lessons.

*　*　*　*

The flower and produce show was in full swing at the village hall. Cora watched proudly as her grandpa put his iced chocolate cake on the display table.

It looked really delicious – almost as good as Margaret's. Mrs Harman thought so, too, when she came to judge it.

"Well, Geoff," she said, "this is quite amazing. I can hardly believe it's one of your cakes."

Grandpa grinned sheepishly.

"I've been having lessons," he told her.

"Well it's certainly paid off. Congratulations."

Cora could hardly contain her excitement as Mrs Harman placed a third-place rosette on Grandpa's name.

"Yes!" she cried, punching the air. "You've done it!" She flung her arms round his waist and hugged him.

Then Grandpa hugged Margaret. He'd been doing quite a lot of that lately, Cora had noticed.

In fact, they had been together so much, it had almost been like having Granny back again, though, of course, no-one could ever replace Granny.

"Who would have thought, this time last year, I would be standing here now with a rosette?" Grandpa said.

Smiling, he turned and took Margaret's hand.

"And it's all thanks to you, Cora. Not only have I baked a winning cake but I've also found a wonderful friend."

Cora glowed with pleasure. Her plan couldn't have worked out better. Something told her the cake lady was going to be around for a long time to come. ■

132

iStock and Alamy.

Equal Rights

DESPITE the fact that Queen Victoria had already been monarch for 32 years, women in Victorian Britain still suffered many legal and social inequalities both inside and outside marriage. The seeds of the movement for more equality between the sexes had already been sown, but in 1869, philosopher and Member of Parliament John Stuart Mill published "The Subjection Of Women", an essay that would create real changes.

Mill, inspired by his late wife Harriet Taylor, argued that:

"The principle which regulates the existing social relations between the two sexes — the legal subordination of one sex to the other — is wrong itself, and now one of the chief hindrances to human improvement; and that it ought to be replaced by a principle of perfect equality, admitting no power or privilege on the one side, nor disability on the other."

He wanted women to have a more equal legal status within marriage and for the right to vote to be extended. His work was controversial at the time, but also important because it was the first time a man in the public eye had taken up the female cause.

The essay encouraged the women's suffrage groups that were forming around the country, and Mill himself became president of the National Society of Women's Suffrage, although it would take another 59 years before full suffrage was achieved. ■

Trick Or Treat?

by Isobel J. Sayer

I HURRIED along the wet street, the shimmering, oily puddles reflecting pale orange from the street lamps above, soggy autumn leaves lying forlornly in their depths. Skirting round the deeper ones in my knee-length black boots, I tucked my scarf more tightly round my neck and thrust my hands deep into my padded jacket pockets.

It was early evening, yet already I could hear the excited shrieks of small children making their way down a nearby street.

I frowned.

I had nothing against Hallowe'en itself – what I objected to was being expected to join in.

Well, they could forget knocking on my door tonight. I had made my plans carefully.

I would turn off the outside light so that the path was dark and uninviting, make sure the curtains were drawn tightly against the late October gloom, and hunker down with a good book.

To all intents and purposes it would look like no-one was home. And if someone thought they would chance it anyway, and did have the temerity to knock and use that interminably annoying yell of "Trick or treat", well, I would just ignore them.

All this imported nonsense from America, it just gets worse every year, I mused. We'll all be forced to celebrate Thanksgiving before we know it.

It was never this commercialised when I was a child, I thought grumpily, fed up with all the cobwebs, pumpkins and scary masks festooning most of the shop windows in town for weeks on end.

I shrugged my coat off inside the chilly hallway of my small house and reached to turn on the light.

Then I drew my hand back swiftly as I remembered my determination not to invite any unwanted sticky-fingered small people anywhere near my door tonight.

I drew my hand away from the switch, and dropped my keys into a dish sitting on the radiator near the door.

A loud meow greeted me, as Jenkins purred his way sinuously round my ankles, leaving trails of tortoiseshell hairs on my tights and my neat black work skirt.

"All right, all right," I muttered, feeling my way along the hall towards the lounge door.

The curtains were open and a faint tangerine glow from the street outside lit up the stark, dark shapes of my sofa, armchairs and coffee table.

The television screen stood blackly in one corner, a tiny red light blinking where I had earlier left it switched on to standby.

I opened the kitchen drawer, feeling for the tin opener, and then resorted to shining the screen of my mobile phone into the drawer to find what I was looking for.

"This is ridiculous," I muttered to myself. "Anyone would think I was a right killjoy."

I bent down to scratch behind Jenkins's ears absentmindedly in the dark.

"I just don't like Hallowe'en," I told him. "It's over-commercialised, and it just feels a bit wrong somehow, dressing small children up as ghouls and witches and sending them round houses basically begging for sweets. I don't see why I should feel obliged to participate, that's all."

Jenkins was unimpressed. He just wanted his dinner.

Keeping my phone screen on to light my way, I filled the cat's food bowl and listened intently.

All I could hear now was the chomping noise he made as he polished off his long-awaited dinner; any sound of activity outside seemed to have passed my road by.

I kicked my boots off and left them in the corner of the kitchen, then helped myself to a can of cola from the larder rather than take one from the fridge and risk the internal light coming on and revealing myself to my imagined observers.

I then padded back into the lounge to draw the curtains tightly against my least favourite evening of the year.

Turning the table lamp down as low as it could go, I opened my book, took a deep draught of vaguely warm fizz straight from the can, and soon managed to lose myself in a realm of hobbits, wizards and Black Riders as I became engrossed in the intriguing fantasy world of Middle Earth and "The Lord Of The Rings".

The irony of my reading choice was lost on me as I settled down for a quiet evening in on my own.

*　　*　　*　　*

The timid knock on my door sounded overly loud in the dim silence of the house. I jumped involuntarily, my heart thudding faster, not helped by the fact that I had been lost in the darkness of Mordor.

I took the bookmark from the back and placed it carefully into the page open in front of me. Shutting the book, I listened intently. Jenkins, curled up beside me, barely stirred.

There it was again, a timid, tentative knock, and a small voice, sounding more pleading than the aggressive pushiness I had been expecting, was stammering a quiet but persistent, "Hello."

I sighed heavily. I would go out there, I decided, and tell them politely but firmly that I didn't believe in Hallowe'en, and that they could leave me alone and try someone else.

I rose to my feet, a vague sense of meanness stealing over me. Would it really hurt to be polite and join in, or would that just encourage them? Would word get around and result in hordes of them on my doorstep every year from now on?

I could end up being labelled as an easy target if I gave them anything tonight.

I remembered cleaning up smashed eggs two years ago, the yellow yolk drying hard on the brickwork, shining dribbles of egg white snaking towards the ground, and small fragments of shell embedded into the glutinous mess. My indignation returned at the memory.

That was when I had decided to ignore all callers the following year and make it look like no-one was home.

It had worked a treat; myself and Jenkins, snuggled indoors, enjoying the quiet of no television for once, and completely undisturbed by unwanted callers.

I felt in my pockets and pulled out a handful of change. I decided I would give them this, if only to prevent the egg or flour reprisal, but was determined that I would send them off with a flea in their ear, and warnings of dire consequences should they dare call on me next year.

"All right, I'm coming," I muttered crossly, as the knocking persisted. I turned on the hall light; at least then whoever it was would hopefully stop that incessant tap, tap, tapping on my door.

I flung it open, prepared to growl my annoyance at them, expecting to see the usual group of young teenagers, outfitted in some half-hearted pretence at a costume, ready to fling flour and egg at my walls unless they got something out of me.

Instead, a tearful little girl, clutching the hand of a child who looked barely old enough to walk, started sobbing.

"I lost Mummy, and we didn't know what to do."

I crouched down in front of the children. How they had found their way up my pitch dark garden path I would never know. The eldest couldn't have been more than about six years old.

"Wait there a minute," I commanded, and ran down the path to the gate.

Drizzle had started again in earnest and peppered my glasses with a fine spray as I glanced both ways along the pavement. There was not a soul in sight.

I returned to the children, who were standing where I had left them.

The little girl was shivering, dressed only in a satin and net black and green witch's dress, one shoulder falling off where the costume was too big for her. A home-made hat adorned with silver foil stars perched at a jaunty angle on top of her fair hair.

The small child next to her, dressed in a spotty dog fleecy onesie, merely sucked its thumb and gazed at me with a serious expression.

"You'd better come in," I told them, thankful that it was my door they had knocked on. Goodness knows where they could have ended up.

I grabbed the cream fleece throw from the back of the sofa and turned up the lamp.

"Here, let me wrap this round you, you're freezing," I said.

She hiccupped and wiped a grubby hand across her face, smearing the tears, so that her red cheeks were now glistening.

The puppy dog onesie child just stared at me, unblinking, as I wrapped the warm throw around the little girl.

"Here, put those down somewhere," I suggested, as I realised each child was still clutching a cheap-looking bucket disguised as a plastic orange and green pumpkin, complete with the obligatory carved tombstone teeth and slanting eyes. A few sweets and coins lay in the bottom of each one.

"They'll be safe here until we find your mummy," I said authoritatively, taking them from their unresisting hands and placing them on to the coffee table.

"Now sit down there, while I phone the police. They'll find your mummy, don't worry."

Two pale faces scrutinised me silently, tears stopped now that a grown-up seemed to be in control.

Jenkins stood up, stretched his back, yawned and promptly climbed into the little girl's lap.

She smiled involuntarily and turned to look up at me, eyes shining with unshed tears.

"He likes me." She turned to the solemn onesie puppy. "Look, Bobby, I've got a witch's cat."

The little girl smoothed out her skirt and Jenkins settled into her lap, kneading and purring and butting her hand with his head until she started to stroke him gently.

The little boy tentatively put out a sticky finger and gently touched the cat's head.

I dithered with the phone in my hand. Was this actually an emergency?

Probably not, really, I thought to myself. The children were safe and warm here, and would be fine with me until their mother was located.

Now what was that other number? That was it – 101.

I smiled at the children in an attempt to appear reassuring as I listened to an automated voice telling me I was in a queue and that my call was important to them.

Onesie Puppy was sucking his thumb, cat hairs and all, no doubt, while the little witch, now quite happy and animated, was chatting in a friendly way to Jenkins.

She was showing him her bucket of treats and was seemingly unaffected by his complete lack of interest.

"Tenth in the queue," I muttered to myself and crouched down next to the girl. I hadn't even found out their names; that would surely be the first thing the operator would ask me.

The little witch grinned at me, a big gap where her two front teeth were missing.

"I'm Lily-Beth and this is my baby brother Bobby. We live at four, Acacia Avenue and my mummy has brown hair and is very pretty."

I chuckled to myself as I prepared to pass this information on to the police as soon as someone answered my call.

Perhaps I should have dialled 999; maybe they would class this as an emergency.

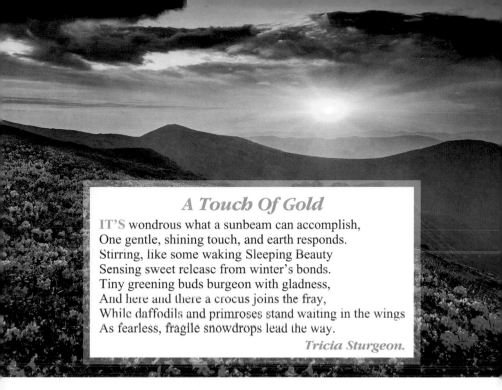

A Touch Of Gold

IT'S wondrous what a sunbeam can accomplish,
One gentle, shining touch, and earth responds.
Stirring, like some waking Sleeping Beauty
Sensing sweet release from winter's bonds.
Tiny greening buds burgeon with gladness,
And here and there a crocus joins the fray,
While daffodils and primroses stand waiting in the wings
As fearless, fragile snowdrops lead the way.

Tricia Sturgeon.

After all, there was no doubt a distraught mother out there somewhere, probably at the police station already, fearful and panicking at the loss of her two children in the dark.

"Please continue to hold. Your call is important to us; you are number four in the queue."

"Can I eat a sweetie?" a small voice piped up, his hood now pushed back to reveal a mop of fair hair. Bobby was clearly feeling more confident.

He hopped off the sofa and picked up one of the plastic pumpkins.

Lily-Beth rebuked him sternly, in the authoritative way that only big sisters can.

"Mummy said we were not allowed to eat anything until she says so," she stated firmly, taking the bucket from his hand and placing it next to her, out of his reach.

"I only want to *hold* the lolly," he said plaintively and the little girl gave a dramatic sigh.

"Just one then, and only holding it. No unwrapping it, Bobby, do you hear me?"

He grinned and hopped off the sofa to help himself to a wrapped lollipop from inside the pumpkin.

He clutched it in one chubby little hand and scooted himself back until he was sitting snuggled up to his sister, big blue eyes now drooping with tiredness

iStock.

as his thumb went back into his mouth.

Finally my call was answered.

"Yes, we have the mum here at the police station. We'll send an officer round with her directly."

"Mummy's on her way," I announced brightly, and sat down opposite the two children, my fleece still wrapped around Lily-Beth, Jenkins kneading her lap, and Bobby now curled up asleep next to them both, lolly still clutched tightly in his hand.

I wondered if I should offer her something to eat or drink, but on balance decided against it, what with all the allergies children seemed to be prone to these days.

Anyway, she seemed content, absentmindedly stroking the cat and staring at me with large blue eyes framed by the longest lashes I had ever seen, darkened with the recent tears.

"What happened, Lily-Beth? How did you lose Mummy?" I asked, glancing at my watch and wondering how long I would need to entertain this small child for.

She wriggled and sat further upright, dislodging Jenkins somewhat as he slid forward on the satin skirt of her dress.

She scooped him up in her arms, and he dangled there patiently, a pair of small arms clutched around his middle as she kissed the top of his head. I was surprised how tolerant he was being.

I jumped up.

"Here, why don't you sit further back, and we can put the fleece on your lap, and that way he won't slide off so easily."

She allowed me to lift him out of her arms and move the fleece from her shoulders to her lap and settle Jenkins on.

He resumed his contended kneading, now on the fleece rather than the slippery fabric of her costume.

Lily-Beth was still talking animatedly about their evening, all sense of distress gone, when the police knocked on the door.

A tear-stained young woman hugged me effusively, then I showed her to the lounge where Lily-Beth was continuing her tale to a rather disinterested Jenkins, and Bobby was fast asleep, lolly in one hand and his other thumb tucked firmly in his mouth.

*   *   *   *

I have already decided that next year the path will be well lit, and a box of goodies by the front door with something special for Lily-Beth and Bobby, who have made their mother promise to let them visit again.

And who knows, maybe there will even be a carved pumpkin or two at the gate to invite other little ghouls and ghosties in. ■

Muckross House, Killarney

IT won't be long before you feel as if you are turning back the hands of time when you step inside Muckross House, situated just a few miles from Killarney town centre,.

This 19th-century mansion, designed by the Scottish architect William Burn, was built for Henry Arthur Herbert and his wife Mary Balfour Herbert, the watercolourist, who gave some paintings to Queen Victoria. The royal visitor stayed in one of the 65 rooms at Muckross House during a state visit to Killarney in 1861.

The house changed ownership, and in 1932 Muckross House and its estate was given to the Irish nation, forming the basis of present-day Killarney National Park. The gardens of the grand house include the Arboretum which houses many plants from the southern hemisphere, and there is also a sunken garden. ■

A Spot Of Baking

by Pamela Ormondroyd

LTHOUGH two full years have passed, it seems like only yesterday that Violet Webb was pacing up and down her kitchen in the very same manner as she is today. Two years ago the weather was very much the same as it is today. It was raw and blustery then, too, with bleak winter covering the garden in her usual dull, grey shroud, making skeletons of the silver birches and browbeating any struggling new bud into submission.

Violet looks out of the rear window, across the fields to the village beyond. No birds or people are brave enough to venture out today and the only movement is from swaying bare branches and falling twigs.

She holds on to the worktop and bites her lip as a feeling of helplessness sweeps through her.

Just a few minutes before, Ken had rung again.

"Any news, love?" The quiet, reassuring voice of her husband has already broken into the deathly silence three times that morning. How she wishes he was here at home with her.

"No, not yet. I promise I'll be in touch the moment I hear."

"Are you all right, Vi? I'm trying to put my foot down, love, but there seem to be more roadworks this week than ever, I'm afraid."

"I'm fine, really I am, Ken. And don't you go too fast, now. I don't want to be worrying about you, too." There was a slight pause. "I'm going to do a spot of baking."

"Ah," Ken said. She could almost see his knowing smile. "That's a good idea."

Three times he has called, but she is now no further on. It's so difficult to concentrate on anything. Yet, Violet knows that a spot of baking is the very best thing for her.

Even from an early age she has found the whole process of preparing, measuring, sifting and kneading in a warm, safe kitchen entirely therapeutic.

When the going gets tough, a baking session eases her aching head, helps her switch off for a while and relax. She can switch on the radio and sing along, unheard, as she immerses herself in the familiar, rhythmic, routine tasks. So

Illustration by Philip Crabb.

today, of all days, the sanctuary of her kitchen is the only place to be.

Violet sits down at the long wooden table and picks up the old brown recipe book, the contents of which she practically knows off by heart.

Now battered and stained and held together by a thick rubber band, the book still holds surprises and golden treasures within its pages.

Forgotten memories of particular birthday cakes and parties, of Christmas puddings and families round the tree, of celebration buffets and sparkling wine. It is like holding the hand of a very dear friend.

*   *   *   *

Her son Nigel's brief phone call came at seven a.m. that morning.

"I'm taking Leona in, Mum. The pains have started."

There was a short silence. A quick intake of breath.

"Are you sure, love? I mean, she's still got four weeks to go."

"Can't risk it, Mum." He sounded nervous, his voice high-pitched. "Look, try not to worry. I'll let you know what happens."

Try not to worry. It was no use. Her heart was already in her mouth. And Ken was still half a day away. She could have ordered a taxi, of course, but then Nigel might prefer to be on his own just now, to concentrate solely on his wife. Better to stay put for the moment where people could find her.

Violet gazes across to the window-sill and at the silver-framed photograph of Nigel and Leona taken on their wedding day. Didn't they look wonderful?

She remembers Leona entering this kitchen many years ago for the very first time and sitting nervously at the table. Violet took to the pretty, gentle teenager at once and their relationship had flourished from the start.

Leona laughed as she told Violet that she hadn't made one edible cake in her life, so Violet willingly taught her to bake, from basic things like biscuits and jam tarts to lemon drizzles and rich sponge puddings.

And while they chatted as the radio carried on in the background, together they baked an engagement cake, and later, a more ambitious two-tiered wedding one.

And as the pair became easier with each other Violet told Leona how she and Ken had yearned for a child of their own.

That for years she kept a satin-soft christening robe, waiting for that something special to happen, but which sadly never did.

And that when the adoption agency finally found them their special little boy and made their dreams come true, Nigel was already nearly two and much too big to wear it.

"Well, Nigel and I hope to have a child one day, Violet," Leona said, putting a friendly arm around Violet's shoulder. "Maybe more than one."

*   *   *   *

Two years before, on a damp, dreary morning just like this, Violet was breathlessly pacing her kitchen floor, waiting for news. Nigel rang her just before six a.m. to tell her that Leona was in some pain and that he was taking her into hospital.

Despite the battering of the rain against the window, Violet took down her cookery book and thumbed through the pages. Soon, despite her shaking hands and rapidly beating heart, a dozen small rolls and a wholemeal loaf were rising gently in the oven.

The phone call from her son came just a few hours later and she knew immediately from the tone of his voice that the news wasn't good.

Afterwards, her friends reminded Violet that miscarriages were quite common, often there was no reason, and that the couple would almost certainly be proud parents one day.

But for Violet their words of comfort fell on empty ears. She had been through it all. She knew.

So, two years ago, all through that particular February and into March, the kitchen was dark, the oven mostly cold.

Now, today, two years on, the air in the kitchen is more subdued and the radio plays at a whisper while Violet wipes the worktop surfaces.

She has sausage rolls cooling on the worktop and a meat and onion pie wrapped up in cling film.

On the outside she looks calm and competent, but inside she feels slightly nauseous and faint, and every now and again she has to stop to steady herself.

She tries to remember Leona's words; how her daughter-in-law has many times tried to reassure her.

"The chances of it happening again are virtually nil, Violet. The hospital have monitored me constantly this time and I've had my feet up at home for the past two months."

But the scenario is virtually the same. Even though Leona has made it to thirty-six weeks of her pregnancy and is looking well, she has still gone into hospital too early.

So Violet washes the pots and rearranges the cupboards and copes as best she can. And she looks across at the photograph on the window and the faces are all a blur.

She looks past the picture and out into the garden where, all of a sudden, her misty eyes focus on a lazy sun which has begun to poke through the thick grey cloud.

And as she gazes, a smidgen of light bounces off one of the bronze leaves still on the tree. Temporarily, for just a split second, her heart lifts. Nature always finds a way, carries on.

Just then the phone rings, loudly and aggressively, making her jump.

She walks slowly to the receiver, swallowing hard and clearing her throat. "Nigel?"

"It's a girl, Mum! Just over six pounds and she's perfect. You should hear the lungs on her! And Leona's fine, too. Tired, of course, but ecstatic. Oh, I can't believe it, Mum. I'm a father!"

And her son rambles on, overjoyed, and she can barely keep up with him.

Violet puts down the receiver, her heart beating twenty to the dozen.

Suddenly she is walking on air; feathery, floating like one of her lightest sponges.

"Yes, you're a father, my darling. And I'm a granny," she whispers.

She returns to the kitchen and checks on the oven and returns the cookery book to the shelf. One day soon, she will thumb through the pages once more and find the recipe for a christening cake.

But no, she's getting ahead of herself. She must first enjoy this magical day.

Tears of relief and happiness roll down Violet's cheeks. She must ring Ken and give him the wonderful news, and tell him that at last they will both be able to hold a newborn baby in their arms.

And then she will go upstairs and take out the christening robe, singing at the top of her voice. ■

© Sainsbury Archive, Museum of London Docklands, and iStock.

Sainsbury's

DRURY LANE in the centre of London seemed the ideal site to set up a small dairy shop to young John James Sainsbury and his wife Mary Ann Staples.

In those days, when produce had to be transported into the city from outlying areas with no refrigeration, quality could be a serious problem, and a lack of hygiene could even result in sickness.

Mary was the daughter of a dairy-shop owner and knew the importance of scrupulous cleanliness. She would get up early to scrub the store every day, and the couple stored fresh produce in the cool basement to keep it fresh for longer.

John Sainsbury even came up with the idea of asking the Dutch suppliers of the store's butter to stamp the date of production on the packets. This impressed the Dutch government so much they later made it compulsory. With quality taken care of, the couple also made their prices competitive, so they were able to adopt the slogan "Quality perfect, prices lower."

In time, customer loyalty enabled them to open more shops and expand their range of products, even offering own-brand goods.

Over the next 150 years, Sainsbury's grew to become one of the big four supermarkets operating in Britain today. ∎

Illustration by Jim Dewar

The Portrait

by Donald Lightwood

I 'M off now – sure you don't mind?" Elspeth said to her husband, Frank, pottering behind the counter in his DIY shop.

"No, off you go. You deserve a birthday treat. You can get ready for the big do tonight."

"Forty-one is nothing special," she said.

"Just you wait!" he promised.

She laughed and kissed him across the counter. She enjoyed helping out in the shop, but it was a treat to get the afternoon off.

"Bye!" she called out.

She had no plan for her free time and she wandered the quiet afternoon streets. How good it was to feel happy!

Frank was her second husband and their two-year marriage had worked better than she'd dared hope after her first experience.

With the sun in her eyes, she didn't see the A-board on the pavement until she almost fell over it. It was an advert for the local art club's exhibition and on impulse she decided to go in.

It seemed Elspeth was the only visitor. A woman was arranging a painting on an easel at the far end, but that was it.

The club used an old church hall that provided a large space to show off their work. An information leaflet told her that the exhibition was the result of their annual competition and was a mixture of landscapes, still life and a few portraits.

The bulk of the pictures were of the countryside and nearby villages. They all looked good to Elspeth, but there was such a variety of views and subjects that she wondered how on earth the judges had been able to decide which one was the best.

However, as she moved around, she realised the woman was placing one painting on an easel a little apart from the rest. This must be the winner, she guessed.

It was a portrait, and as she got closer to it, Elspeth halted in astonishment. The painting was of her ex-husband, Edward. There was no doubting it. There was even the mole on his cheek, the one he used to curse when he was shaving.

"Hello," the woman said. "Not many people today, I'm afraid."

"Everyone's probably making the most of the sun," Elspeth responded. "So this is the winning picture?"

The lady nodded.

"Yes. I think it's the first time a portrait has won."

Elspeth smiled.

"It's very good."

"I'm glad you like it." The woman was about the same age as Elspeth, and dressed in neat blue jeans and a colourful top.

"Is the model a member of the art club?" Elspeth asked.

She couldn't believe the club would appeal to Edward. Art had never been his thing.

The woman grinned.

"Oh, gosh, no. He's much more interested in golf."

"You know him?"

The woman shrugged and gave a big smile.

"Actually, I painted it."

"Really? You're extremely talented."

"Thank you. But I'm lucky. My husband is very understanding and I get plenty of time for my art." She nodded at the portrait. "So I painted him for his Christmas present."

Elspeth took a breath.

"He's your husband?"

"Yes, he is."

Elspeth hesitated.

"Then you must be Frances," she said after a moment.

"That's right. How did you . . .?"

"Edward used to be married to me."

Frances gasped.

"You're Elspeth?"

"Yes."

Frances looked uncertain suddenly.

"I don't know what to say."

"You're the last person I ever wanted to meet," Elspeth said. She looked at the portrait and then at Frances. "You took my husband away from me."

Frances gave a slow shake of the head.

"That isn't how it was."

Elspeth made an impatient gesture.

"He left me for you."

"That's true," Frances conceded, "but there were good reasons why he chose to do that."

"Oh? And what were they?" Elspeth said bitterly. "Your irresistible charm, perhaps?"

"I think you know what they were, Elspeth."

There was a silence, both of them aware that they were about to stir up the past.

"Edward was the love of my life," Elspeth burst out. "Until you came along."

Frances looked at her keenly.

"I was simply working as his secretary – it's not as though I hunted him down."

"Maybe not, but you were conveniently available."

Frances spoke more gently.

"Didn't it ever occur to you that if Edward had been happily married to you, it would never have happened?"

Elspeth coloured.

"We had our difficulties, like any married couple. No-one's relationship is perfect, after all."

Frances hesitated before she spoke.

"Believe me, I felt for you, losing the baby."

Elspeth had hoped having a child would bring the two of them closer together. Losing the baby before it had been born had shattered them. She'd clung to Edward. What else could she have done?

"It wasn't easy," she said stiffly.

She knew he had been glad to escape to the office each morning, worn out by her obsessive, possessive behaviour.

"You said Edward gives you lots of time for your art," Elspeth went on. "It might be the 1980s, but he was always old-fashioned about wives not working."

"Like you, I had plenty of time, but I didn't have anything constructive to do with it apart from housework and caring for him.

"In a way, I cared too much for him. I believed having a baby was the ideal solution. But, of course, it didn't work out that way. And with you waiting in the wings . . ."

"There's nothing to be gained from being bitter," Frances interrupted her. "It's over and done with." She waited a moment. "I see you got married again."

Elspeth automatically placed her right hand over her wedding ring. She nodded.

"Yes, two years ago."

"That's good. I imagine you're happy now."

Elspeth looked at her wryly.

"I think you're guessing and hoping to change the subject."

Frances's face crinkled into a smile.

"Could be. But I hope I'm right."

"I'm married to Frank and yes, we're happy. We work together in his shop," Elspeth told her.

"I'm glad. And for what it's worth, so are Edward and I," Frances said. "Come on, let's have a cup of tea, shall we?"

They sat in a small room off the hall.

"Thank heavens for teabags," Frances said, busying herself with the kettle and mugs. "They make life so much easier."

Elspeth found herself in a curious state; she didn't know what to feel. The shock of finally meeting Frances was confusing.

It was clear she was a pleasant and talented person, but it was impossible to forget how they had been brought together.

And yet she could understand already that Frances wasn't the kind of woman to relish being cast in the role of the "other woman".

Knowing she had taken another woman's husband must have nagged at her. However, that both women were now more happily married came as a kind of blessing.

"Judging by this portrait, you could have become an artist," Elspeth said.

Frances pulled a face.

"It's a long story. My parents believed a job in insurance would be more stable."

"And you ended up painting the boss."

"I know, it's ironic," Frances agreed. "He wasn't the easiest of models. He talked all the time and just wouldn't sit still."

"That was Edward," Elspeth said, amused. "I tried buying him one of those Rubik's Cubes to slow him down for a bit."

Frances smiled.

"Still, apart from that, we get along."

Elspeth put her mug down.

"After we separated I tried not to think about him. And, of course, I didn't want to think about you.

"Getting you out of my mind became obsessive – that's the word Edward often used about me." She paused for a moment. "Selling wallpaper and paint in my husband's shop has worked wonders. And being happy now, I suppose."

"You know, I'm glad we've finally met," Frances said. "Though I'm sure if anyone had suggested it to either of us, we probably wouldn't have agreed to do it."

Elspeth nodded.

"You can blame my birthday," she said with a smile. "Frank gave me the afternoon off as a treat. I bumped into your sign, and here I am."

"My grandmother would have said it was meant," Frances said.

Elspeth frowned.

"I wouldn't normally go along with that, but I can't help wondering. That portrait . . ."

"If I hadn't painted it . . . But we could go on all day like this, guessing, speculating," Frances said. She gave a bright smile. "Now you know about us, you could always join the art club."

Elspeth shook her head.

"Oh, I'm not artistic in the least. I do a bit of embroidery now and then, but that's it."

"We have a needlework group," Frances cajoled.

"I couldn't – not with Edward's portrait staring at me."

"Ah, but that will disappear after the exhibition."

Elspeth nodded and glanced through the open door at the hall full of paintings.

"And I think we should, too – disappear, I mean. Thankfully it seems we've each found the right man. Let's leave it at that."

"You're probably right," Frances agreed. "And by the way – happy birthday."

"Thank you. I can safely say it's one I won't forget. Good to meet you, Frances."

And with that she stepped back out into the sunlight. She would go and buy a couple of special cakes and take them back to the shop.

She and Frank could share them as a birthday treat with their afternoon cuppa. ■

Lochinver

BUILT on the shores of Loch Inver, this village in the Assynt district of Sutherland is one of the busiest harbours in the Highlands. In fact, fishing is a vital source of employment, along with tourism.

The area attracts hillwalkers keen to explore the natural beauty, and fitness levels can be tested by scaling Suilven, which rises sharply to 731 metres, making it one of the most distinctive mountains in Scotland.

If you have sea legs, however, cruises bring a different perspective and you have the chance to see dolphins and seals – even the occasional minke and killer whale have been spotted here! Birdlife is plentiful, with everything from puffins to oystercatchers. Keep your eyes on the sky and you may be lucky enough to spot a golden eagle, too. ■

Illustration by Helen Welsh.

Leah's List

by Keith Havers

NOW then, where did I put it? Ah, yes, here it is."

Leah swept aside all the other junk that lay at the bottom of her bedside drawer and pulled out the little black book she had been hunting for.

Sitting on the edge of the bed, she flicked through the first few pages of notable dates, conversion tables and international dialling codes until she reached what she was looking for: January the first.

"I started off with such good intentions," she said to herself.

The words that she had written neatly that day stared back up at her accusingly.

1. Run a marathon

2. Learn a language

3. Write a novel

"It's nearly midsummer and I haven't done any of the things I promised myself I'd do. I haven't even made a start."

Last year Leah's friend, Wendy, had taken part in the local marathon with her boyfriend and had raised almost five hundred pounds for charity in the process.

Leah remembered her coming into the office every day before the big event talking about how many miles of training she had done the night before and what energy supplements she had been taking to enhance her performance and her fitness.

She bored everybody to death, but at least she was doing something worthwhile, Leah thought.

A few weeks after that, Wendy and her boyfriend had gone on holiday together to the Canary Islands, but not before taking a few evening classes in conversational Spanish.

"I want to be able to at least order a meal and drinks in the local language," she had said.

As far as Leah was concerned, it didn't make sense to go to all that trouble when English was so widely spoken. She did have to admit, however, that hearing Wendy reel off phrase after phrase in a foreign accent was very impressive.

"I did French at GCSE," she recalled. "Maybe I could take that up."

Of course, when Wendy returned to work, there were the photos to be passed around the office and tales of romantic meals by the ocean and strolls along the beach to be told.

But not only that. Wendy announced blithely that, while they were away, she had begun writing a book – a modern romance set in an exotic location by the sea.

Leah couldn't believe it would ever get published. Nevertheless, she couldn't deny that it would be an awesome achievement just to put enough words on paper to make a full-blown novel.

"I'll take a walk," she said to herself, slipping on her jacket. "Maybe that will clear my mind."

It was a pleasant evening with just a few clouds in the sky and a light breeze. Leah set off at a brisk pace down the hill and turned on to the canal path.

Half a mile further on she passed by the beer garden of the Navigation Inn and noted how busy it was.

She stepped to one side as a couple of joggers, a youth and a girl, came by in the opposite direction. They seemed so relaxed in their easy stride and upright posture.

"That's what I should be doing." Leah sighed. "Great, now I feel guilty again."

She was almost past the area of parasols and wooden benches when she heard a call.

"Leah! Over here!"

She turned to see her friend, Gavin, standing up and waving. Weaving between the hordes of drinkers, she joined him at one of the smaller tables and sat down opposite him.

"Hi, Gavin. Is Kate not with you?"

"She didn't feel like coming out tonight so I'm here on my own."

Gavin and Kate were old friends of Leah's from their college days. They had been a couple for just over a year but still met up with Leah every now and again. Gavin got her a white wine from the bar and settled back in his chair.

"So what are you doing out and about on your own?" he said.

Leah explained about her exasperation at getting nowhere with her New Year resolutions. She told him all about Wendy and her achievements.

"Sounds as if she likes to brag about herself a bit," Gavin said. "But you shouldn't compare yourself to someone at work. Not everybody is so active. You shouldn't feel bad about it."

"You're in a running club, aren't you, Gavin?"

"Yes. But I haven't run a marathon."

"You do charity runs and races. That's something."

"Why don't you join my club, then? We have plenty of women there. Kate's a member, too."

"Would I be able to train for a marathon?" Leah wanted to know.

"Well, let's see . . . There are a few at the beginning of autumn, but after that I don't know. It only gives you about three months. Maybe you should leave it until next year."

"Oh." The disappointment on Leah's face must have been clear to see.

"Why don't you aim for something smaller? A ten kilometre run, or even five. There are plenty of those going on."

Leah considered Gavin's suggestion. On reflection, a marathon did seem too much for a beginner. A shorter event was the sensible thing to go for.

"I'm not sure about joining a club, though," she said. "I'd feel a bit out of place."

"Why don't you come out with me and Kate? We can take you for a jog around the park, and in a few weeks' time, once you've gained some confidence, you can think about joining up then."

"Sounds great."

"OK. Meet us by the gates at seven tomorrow. Bring some water and a towel."

"Maybe I should make this one my last for a while," she said as she finished off her glass of wine.

* * * *

Leah felt conspicuous the next evening as she stood waiting for her friends just inside the park. The only kit she had managed to dig out was a mismatched pair of shorts and baggy T-shirt.

She had draped her towel around her neck and carried a small plastic drinks bottle.

Her trainers were an old pair that she used for pottering around the bit of garden at the back of her flat. Mrs Parsons in the apartment below couldn't cope with all the bending down and lifting any more so Leah often went down to keep things tidy. Now the trainers were caked in dirt and the laces were frayed.

"If they don't turn up soon I'm going home," she muttered.

Then Gavin appeared at the end of the road. In his club vest with its logo emblazoned across the front, tight Lycra shorts and stylish trainers, he looked every inch an athlete.

"Where's Kate?" Leah said as he eased to a halt, hardly out of breath.

"She's resting up tonight. Saving herself for tomorrow's club run."

"I haven't got any proper running gear."

"What you have on will do fine," he reassured her. "You might want to think about a decent pair of trainers when you enter a road race. We'll stick to running on grass for now."

Leah thought Gavin was getting too far ahead, talking about races and brand-new trainers, but she let it go. Right now all she wanted to do was a lap of the park and go home. They jogged along the path until they reached a bench.

"First we ought to do some warm-up exercises," Gavin said.

That wasn't what Leah had expected.

Gavin made her spend five minutes with him, stretching her muscles and getting her body warmed up.

Eventually they set off at a slow pace and, with a combination of running and walking, Leah managed two laps.

"You did well," Gavin said. "You'll probably feel a little stiff tomorrow but that's normal. Have a bath tonight, rest tomorrow night and come out for another run the day after."

Although she had barely run a mile in total, Leah felt that she had at least made a start on her resolutions.

"I'll jog with you back to your flat," Gavin said. "Then I can put in a few miles before going home."

They took a gentle trot back to Leah's and arrived just as Mrs Parsons was putting out her rubbish.

"Here, let me do that for you!" Leah called as she took the bulging bin bag from the old lady and lifted the lid of the wheelie bin.

Gavin gave her a quizzical look.

"Mrs Parsons is almost completely deaf," she explained. "You have to speak quite loudly."

"I see."

"She keeps giving me those hand signals, you know, trying to sign, but I only know 'yes', 'no' and 'maybe'."

"Well, don't forget what I said about soaking in the bath. See you in a couple of days, same time."

Leah watched him set off at a speed that she could only dream about. It was obvious that their two laps of the park had been a mere stroll for him.

"Come on, Mrs Parsons!" she said. "I'll walk you to your door!"

*　　*　　*　　*

Leah felt less self-conscious on her second session with Gavin. She did more running and less walking on their two laps, so Gavin suggested they have a sit down before doing one more circuit.

"I've really enjoyed tonight," she said. "I think I'll start looking for a five kilometre race to enter. Maybe me and Kate could do one together."

"I think Kate has given up running."

"Really?"

"The truth is," Gavin said, "we're not going out together any more."

"Oh, that's a shame. I'm sorry."

"We didn't have a big bust-up or anything. We just agreed to stop seeing each other."

"I like Kate," Leah said.

"There's no reason why you two can't still be friends," Gavin said.

They completed their third lap and agreed to meet up at the weekend for a longer session.

*　　*　　*　　*

"You did that last lap without having to slow down for a walk," Gavin said on Sunday morning after pausing for their first break.

"I'm finding it a lot easier now. I'd never have managed to get this far without your help."

"It's been fun."

"I still have my other goals to go for," Leah said. "Taking up running was just the first one."

"You mean the foreign language and the writing? Can't help you with those, I'm afraid."

"Perhaps I could join a night class at the college."

"The courses don't start until after the summer holidays, though. You won't be able to enrol until September."

"I'm hopeless, aren't I?"

They sat for a while drinking from their water bottles until Gavin turned to Leah.

"There is maybe one thing you could try."

"What's that?"

"You said you don't understand the sign language that Mrs Parsons uses. Why don't you learn BSL?"

"BSL?"

"British Sign Language. It would be something useful and you don't have to go on holiday to use it."

"Gavin, that's a brilliant idea!"

"I'm sure you could make a start by getting a book from the library. There must be a course you can go on when you're ready."

"I'll look on the internet when I get home," Leah said.

"As for the writing," Gavin went on, "why don't you start a blog?"

Leah stared at him.

"A blog?"

"You could use it as a journal and log your progress with the running and the sign language. You'd get a bigger audience than just showing off at work. It might inspire people to follow your example."

* * * *

So Leah joined the athletics club, learned how to converse with her neighbour without yelling her head off and began recording her achievements on leahsresolutions.com.

She felt so proud as she crossed the finish line in her club kit and shiny new trainers after completing her first race.

"You did fantastic, sweetheart," Gavin said.

By the end of September Leah's revised list, written on July 1, had a tick after each item.

1. Complete a 5km run

2. Learn BSL

3. Start a blog

4. Get a boyfriend

On Bonfire Night Gavin took her to a firework display and then on to an Italian restaurant. Leah was so happy as he walked her home.

"Next year I'm definitely going to do that marathon," she declared.

"I hope your office colleague doesn't take up triathlon or skydiving," Gavin said. "I don't think I could cope."

Leah shook her head.

"Didn't I tell you?" she said. "Wendy's taking guitar lessons. She brings it in to the office sometimes and practises at lunchtime."

"I can't help you with that," Gavin said. "How about I buy you a mouth organ?"

"Thanks, but don't bother," she replied, laughing. "My days of trying to keep up with Wendy are definitely over. From now on you're all the inspiration I need." ■

The National Wallace Monument

ON September 11, 1869, the 572nd anniversary of William Wallace's famous victory at the Battle of Stirling Bridge, the National Wallace Monument was handed over to its custodians.

Plans to commemorate Scotland's hero had been ongoing since 1818, when Glasgow was proposed as the location. Edinburgh, Scotland's capital, was not keen on that idea and a compromise location in Stirling was agreed.

The competition to design the monument was won by Edinburgh-born Glasgow architect J.T. Rochead, and building began in 1861, with the foundation stone being laid on Bannockburn Day, June 24. At the time, it cost over £10,000, all funded by public subscription.

The monument is situated on the Abbey Craig, a hilltop two miles north of the city. It was from here, in 1297, that Wallace watched the English army approach over Stirling Bridge before leading his own forces to meet them in victorious battle.

The Gothic tower is one of Scotland's most celebrated and recognisable landmarks. The 220-feet-high structure attracts more than 100,000 visitors every year, many of whom climb the 246 steps to enjoy the magnificent views from the top.

On the way up, visitors can pause on each of the floors to enjoy exhibitions celebrating significant moments in Scotland's history and the achievements of remarkable Scottish heroes and heroines. ∎

iStock

Good Timing

by Glenise Lee

I WATCHED him coming towards me, sparks of light from the glitter ball falling on to his dark, Brylcreemed hair. He looked cool. Unbuttoning his jacket, he stopped in front of me. He gave me a quick, shy smile.

"I'm Michael. Would you like to dance?"

I looked him up and down. To be quite honest, I didn't really feel like dancing, though normally I loved it.

My friend had stood me up and I wasn't in a good mood. Sylvia said she'd meet me inside the Palais. I looked towards the door for the fiftieth and definitely the last time. No sign of her.

Looking back at the young man, nervously waiting for my answer, I thought, I might as well.

He held out his hand and led me on to the floor. He wasn't anything to write home about, but I liked the warmth of his smile and his eyes were the brightest of blues.

And he could dance. I doubted I'd be going home with sore toes.

We waltzed, we quick-stepped. We did the Gay Gordons, the Valetta and even tackled a bit of foxtrot. That was a disaster and we ended up stumbling off the dance floor in fits of laughter.

He bought me a drink, a daring Babycham, and as we sat at a table I saw Sylvia bouncing by with her new boyfriend. Spotting me, she mouthed, "Sorry," before the crowd of dancers closed around them.

Once that dance was finished, we waited expectantly to see what was coming next.

The band leader's grin was broad and his teeth gleamed as he announced, to roars of approval, "And now, the latest dance craze to sweep the land."

He said no more, but spun to face his band and raised his arms, giving people time to scramble up from their seats. Then, with a crash, the musicians threw themselves into the March of the Mods.

"Do you know this?" I had to shout.

Michael nodded, finished his half-pint and stood up, doing that thing with his coat button again.

Linking arms, we hit the dance floor, where, arm in arm with all the other dancers, a long line across the floor, we stepped and kicked and laughed and stomped.

At the end of the evening, when the dance hall closed, we met Sylvia and her boyfriend at the bus stop.

She looked my companion up and down.

"Aren't you going to introduce me, Jenny?"

"Sylvia, Michael. Michael, Sylvia," I said, embarrassment warming my cheeks.

"Is that Mick or Mike?" Sylvia asked.

"It's just Michael." He smiled.

The boys saw us safely on to the bus and Sylvia and I travelled home together.

"You stood me up," I said crossly. "Where were you?"

Illustration by Mandy Murray.

Sylvia looked apologetic.

"I was just leaving when Nev arrived and insisted on coming, too. I told him it was a girls' night out and, well, by the time we'd done arguing and he'd insisted . . ." She shrugged. "We were late. Sorry.

"Anyway, seems we did you a good turn. I like your Michael. He seems a good sort."

"He's not my Michael," I protested.

Sylvia raised one eyebrow.

"No?" she said.

Warm-hearted and generous, a little on the chunky side, blonde and slightly dippy, Sylvia was my best friend and often had the infuriating habit of being right. Michael and I were married two years later.

My brother gave me away and as I walked down the aisle, past my sobbing mum, unexpectedly I started to cry, too, missing my dad.

At the altar I needed to borrow Michael's large white handkerchief and blow my nose before proceedings could commence.

After the wedding, we had a great party. Michael remembered his duties as the groom and after dancing with his mum and mine, he asked Sylvia for a dance.

I laughed as he hobbled back to me, groaning.

"My poor feet! You know I love your chief bridesmaid, but she can't dance, can she?"

I grinned.

"No, but she does know how to party."

"Happy, Jenny?" He looked into my eyes and the rest of the world faded away.

My breath caught in my throat and all I could do in return was hold out my hand. He took it and looked at my new gold ring. Folding my fingers, he brushed his knuckles against mine, ring against ring.

"Dance with me always?" he asked.

"I will," I promised.

And our marriage was like a dance. He led and I followed – when I wanted to, that is.

There were times when we were out of step, of course, and often we found ourselves dancing to different tunes.

But with a little bit of shuffling and some syncopation we always found our way back to the same beat.

$$* \quad * \quad * \quad *$$

A year later, Sylvia married Nev. She asked me if I would be her matron of honour.

"You can't be a bridesmaid, not with your baby bump being so big. Even though you look blooming."

"I don't feel blooming," I grumbled. "Except blooming fat."

"So I've got a fat matron of honour. You'll make me look quite svelte." And she hugged me.

For many years after James was born there was little time for dancing, though I often found myself pushing my trolley down a supermarket aisle, stepping slow, slow, quick, quick, slow in time to the canned music.

$$* \quad * \quad * \quad *$$

On my seventieth birthday Michael had planned a special treat for me. My ambition, top of what younger people call their "bucket list", was to dance at the Blackpool Tower ballroom. Again.

For my seventh birthday, Dad had taken us on a day trip to Blackpool. I loved the circus in the Tower. We sat high up.

I'd clung to the arms of my seat, excited but afraid I'd fall down on to the clowns; the tiers were so steep.

Later on, they filled the ring with water and we saw sea-lions performing. Afterwards we went down to the ballroom and I had to mind the baby while Mum and Dad quick-stepped round the floor.

Starlight

IT'S magic on a moonless night,
With silent darkness all around,
To look up at the wondrous sight
As tapestries of stars abound.

The enigmatic Milky Way
In wild and wispy interplay
With diamonds, in silver set,
Like pinholes in a veil of jet.

Dennis W. Turner.

The music was loud, even when the organ disappeared into the stage. I couldn't believe my eyes.

"Where'd it go, Dad?"

He laughed.

"Oh, Reginald Dixon alway does that. I tell you what, we'll have a cup of tea and wait for him to come back up."

Which he did, of course. We heard him playing before we saw him. First the top of his head, then his smile as he half-turned in his seat and winked at his audience.

Dad stood up.

"It's a waltz," he said, holding out his hand. "Would my birthday girl like to dance with me?"

"Can I?" I wasn't sure. The floor was full of strutting adults with sharp elbows stiffly held at eye level, my eye level.

"You're a big girl now, you're seven. Of course you can."

We danced. On the best dance floor in the world, we danced.

Other couples smiled and gave a little girl room to dance with her daddy.

*   *   *   *

So here I was, 63 years later, looking down the length of the Blackpool Tower Ballroom towards the white steps that led up to the stage, where the organist was playing a cha-cha-cha on the massive Wurlitzer organ. It was just like I remembered.

I ached to dance. My toes tapped. My feet twitched so much that I knocked over one of Michael's crutches.

He'd tripped over the cat three weeks before and sprained his ankle; he couldn't walk without pain, let alone dance.

"I'm sorry, love," he said. "But next year. I promise."

I felt guilty for being so miserable. It wasn't Michael's fault, after all, and although we couldn't get up on the floor, we were still here, enjoying the spectacle.

Then I felt a hand on my shoulder. I edged my chair forward, thinking it was someone trying to get past.

"Hiya, Jen."

"Sylvia!" I jumped up in surprise. "What on earth are you doing here?" I think I shrieked with delight. "It's so good to see you, but I thought you were going to Spain?"

She laughed.

"Oh, that was just a big fat lie. Michael wanted to surprise you. You didn't think I'd let you celebrate your birthday without me, did you?" She hugged me.

"I know you want to dance, so grab your handbag and let's pretend we're sixteen again."

"I'm not dancing round my handbag in the Blackpool Tower ballroom." I laughed. "They'd throw us out."

"I'm so glad you said that. We went for a long walk while Michael got you settled and my feet ache. But as he can't dance, maybe you'd like a turn round the floor with Nev?"

At that, Nev shot off to the bar.

"I'll get the drinks."

Light now dawning, I turned to Michael, who had the biggest, widest grin I'd ever seen.

"I suppose it was also a lie that the travel company wouldn't refund the money for the trip?"

He nodded.

"Is that an end to your surprises?"

Michael didn't answer, but his smile became more enigmatic.

I held my breath. Dared I expect more?

A gentle voice spoke in my ear.

"May I have the pleasure of this dance?"

Of course I couldn't refuse the young man who stood behind me holding out his hand. A young man who looked so like his father but with his grandpa's green eyes.

I took his hand and walked into my son's arms. ■

1869 Our Changing World

iStock and Alamy.

The Cutty Sark

BACK in 1869, you could build a world-class ocean-going tea clipper for the princely sum of £16,150. That's how much it cost to construct the *Cutty Sark*, at one time one of the fastest sailing ships on the sea. Now the sole surviving tea clipper, she is listed by National Historic Ships as part of the National Historic Fleet and is a Grade I Listed Monument.

Designed to compete in the annual "tea race", bringing the first of the season's tea to England from China, the ship was built in Glasgow, on the River Clyde, and launched on November 22. Her name is the nickname of Nannie Dee, one of the witches in Robert Burns's poem "Tam O'Shanter", who is depicted in the carved figurehead. "Cutty sark" referred to the immodestly short undergarment worn by the witch when Tam espied her.

The improvements in steam technology meant that sailing ships were gradually replaced by more powerful steamships. The commercial life of the *Cutty Sark* came to an end and, in 1922, retired sea captain Wilfred Dowman bought her for use as a training vessel in Cornwall. Training on the ship ceased in 1954, whereupon she became a museum ship on permanent display at Greenwich.

The *Cutty Sark* has been damaged by fire twice in recent years, but following extensive conservation work, is once more a popular tourist attraction. ■

A Kiss From Santa

by Evelyn Hood

YOU can always tell it's Christmas by the big tree in the town square and the bonnie lights in the high street, and the way the most important buildings are floodlit. And you can tell it's Christmas by the way folk are fighting their way in and out of the shops, weighed down with parcels and weans.

See some of these mothers? When it comes to getting the presents the weans have asked for, and making sure that there's going to be enough to eat over the festive season, even the smallest housewife can be fearsome enough to shake the toughest rugby star out of his boots.

In fact, if one of the weans wanted the rugby star's actual boots for Christmas, the man in question would be well advised to wrap them in glittery paper, slap a bow on them, and get out of it as fast as he could in his stockinged feet.

The people that lived in the tenement had their own way of recognising Christmas. While the piped music in the shopping centre belted out "Chestnuts Roasting On An Open Fire", they were more used to a whiff of Mr McCracken's socks being roasted by an imitation coal-effect gas radiant.

Mr McCracken tended to start hibernating round about mid-December and as his feet were afflicted by bad circulation he liked to get close to the heat.

As for outsiders passing by the tenement – they get their first warning of Christmas when Miss Telford puts her wee artificial tree in her window.

Every December 1 it's in place by nine in the morning, with its silver balls and its wee geriatric fairy slumped against the top.

If a final reminder of the festive season is needed, there are always the carol singers, trawling the closes in twos and threes with one hand permanently held out towards exasperated householders summoned from "EastEnders" and "Coronation Street" during the most exciting scenes.

That's what Christmas is usually like in the tenement. Maybe a few of the folk will exchange cards, or even give a wee gift to the ones they like, or who did them a favour during the past year.

It suits them well enough because they're not the sort of folk to live in their neighbours' pockets.

Illustration by iStock.

So they were a bit taken aback when Mrs Petrie invited them all into her top-floor flat halfway through December, and even more taken aback when she announced the reason for the gathering.

"A tenement party?" Mrs McCracken said doubtfully. "Oh, I don't know about that . . ."

"We usually just have the son and his wife and their bairns round," someone else ventured timidly. "We like it that way."

They were all crowded into the Petrie living-room, perched like budgies on every available space, eating Co-op biscuits and drinking tea.

Mr McCracken was shuffling his feet and looking longingly at the electric coal-effect fire, the width of the room away and taken over by Mr Petrie.

If he but knew it, Mr Petrie was just as miserable, having been hauled from the comfort of his wee garden shed and made to sit by the fire before anyone arrived, so Mr McCracken couldn't pollute the entire flat with his socks.

"You can still have your own folk round – the more the merrier." Mrs Petrie had the loud voice and the confident air of someone who liked to organise other folk and always got her own way.

She was upmarket, having started her working life as sales assistant in the local M&S and reached the dizzy heights of department supervisor by the time she retired.

Her department, she liked to tell anyone who would listen, was run like a tight ship. So was her home, which was why Mr Petrie preferred to spend most of his waking hours in his shed.

"It's just a matter of keeping our doors open so's the whole tenement's like one big house," she explained. "We can go in and out, and as for food, if we all have a wee buffet, folk can have a nibble here and a nibble there."

Poppy Armitage spoke excitedly.

"I think it's a great idea. I'll do some extra baking for it."

Poppy and her husband Colin were the tenement's newlyweds, having recently moved into one of the middle-floor flats.

They hadn't got the hang of tenement life yet – on the days she had access to the washing lines Poppy hung unsuitable underwear out, and she insisted on calling her husband Col, which made Mrs McCracken wince. Mrs McCracken didn't hold with abbreviations, be they names or items of underwear hanging out for all to see.

Poppy was also given to hugging and kissing Colin whenever she felt like it, even on the landing and the stairs.

Today, using the crowded room as an excuse, Poppy was sitting on her husband's knee, her arms about his neck.

"If any of us has extra decorations they could be used on the banisters and the landings," Poppy rushed on. "I'm good at mince-pies – who else wants to volunteer?"

"I will," Miss Telford said eagerly. She liked the idea of a tenement party because her own Christmases tended to be lonely.

"Lovely." Poppy beamed at her, giving Miss Telford the courage to speak up again.

"Perhaps I could persuade some of the children who come carol-singing to form a little choir for the occasion."

"Talking of children, we need a Santa Claus," Poppy said, "to hand out gifts to the tenement children."

"Er – what gifts?" someone asked, alarmed.

"Just wee things – it's the excitement of getting a present that counts. I'll look after that side of it. And Col will be Santa."

"Col won't," a muffled voice said from somewhere in the region of her neck.

"You will so. Say you will or I'll tickle you . . ." Poppy was beginning when Mrs Petrie, appalled by the prospect of unseemly behaviour on the wing chair she had inherited from her Baptist auntie, cut in.

"Colin's quite right, we need someone more mature. Mr Petrie will do it."

All eyes turned to Mr Petrie, who went crimson when he found himself the centre of attention, then white when he realised what his wife had let him in for.

The tenement folk didn't see Mr Petrie all that often, with him being what his wife called an outdoors man.

Mr Petrie loved gardening – he had an allotment, and since being made redundant in his early sixties he had more or less taken over the tenement back court, turning the old shed into a cosy little retreat from the world.

"I don't know about that, Annie," he said feebly now.

"You'll do it. I'll get the outfit," she rapped back at him, and it was all arranged.

✳   ✳   ✳   ✳

Once the tenement dwellers got used to the idea it began to take hold. Extra, unwanted decorations were brought out and used to brighten up the stairways and all the women undertook to bake a little more than usual so that there would be plenty to go around.

Mr Petrie was dragged from his shed at least once a day to practise saying, "Ho, ho, ho," though there wasn't much enthusiasm in it.

Miss Telford was having a lovely time. She and Poppy Armitage had discovered a shared love of music, and while they baked together in Poppy's crowded little kitchen they sang carols.

The only fly in Miss Telford's ointment was that the carol-singing group she had hoped to put together was slow in materialising.

The children who came into the close in the hope of earning some Christmas money were appalled to be warmly welcomed when they knocked at her door, and, worse still, hauled inside.

Home-made mince-pies were thrust into hands outstretched for coins and they listened in horror as their captor told them what a good time they would have as a proper choir, singing proper carols properly.

Poor Miss Telford found herself talking to thin air every time, with nothing to show that children had been standing on her carpet just a moment earlier but a faint whiff of panic in the air.

"Never mind," Poppy consoled her when the carol singers suddenly stopped calling, "we'll have our own singsong on Christmas Day."

✳   ✳   ✳   ✳

Apart from the carol-singers it looked as though everything was going to be perfect. Everyone began to look forward to the party, though little did they realise that the entire tenement was like the *Titanic*, carrying its innocent pleasure-seeking residents towards the lurking iceberg.

The collision happened exactly a week before the party, when the McCrackens' daughter Tricia arrived at her mother's door, a suitcase in one hand, her four-month-old baby on the other arm and her pretty face blotched with tears.

"I've left him, Mammy," she sniffled.

"It had to happen," her mother said as the taxi-driver came puffing up the stairs, laden to the eyebrows with baby necessities. "I always knew it was a mistake, you and him. Never you mind, pet, we're here for ye."

Her husband Douglas arrived five minutes later, before Tricia was halfway through her first cup of tea.

"I have to see her," he said when Mrs McCracken opened the door.

"Over my dead body." The light of battle was in her eyes. She had been training for this situation since the day her Tricia had admitted that she was expecting, and that she and Douglas were going to get married as soon as possible.

"It's just a wee storm in a teacup," he said desperately.

"I knew it wouldnae work out between you. I told our Tricia at the time and I was right."

"Mebbe if you'd kept quiet things would have worked out fine," Douglas said, and knew as soon as the door slammed shut in his face that he should have kept quiet, too.

He turned away and trudged upstairs to the next floor to seek consolation from his aunt, Annie Petrie.

"It had to happen," she said, pouring tea. "I knew it was a mistake, you and her. What went wrong?"

"I don't know. She's changed since the wee one arrived," Douglas said helplessly. "It's been difficult, with a baby in the flat and me trying to study for my exams."

"He was never good enough for you," Mrs McCracken said, at almost the same moment Mrs Petrie was saying, "She was never good enough for you. You deserved better."

Neither Tricia nor Douglas replied; instead, Tricia stared at the floor, thinking about the way a kiss from Douglas Jardine could curl her toes, while Douglas stared at the floor and remembered the feel and the smell and the sheer joy of holding Tricia close.

"But what actually happened?" Mrs Petrie and Mrs McCracken were asking.

What had happened was that Tricia decided that she wanted an eternity ring for her Christmas, and Douglas couldn't afford to buy one.

"I should think not," Mrs Petrie said warmly. "You're still a student. She's lucky you put a wedding ring on her finger, without expecting anything more."

"I always knew he was selfish," Mrs McCracken was saying. "He takes after that snobby auntie of his. And that's the end of this daft Christmas party she wants us to have. I'll have nothing to do with it now."

"No, Mammy." Tricia wiped her tears away, took the Empire biscuit then passed the plate to her father. 'I'll not see your tenement party ruined just because of me and Douglas."

''You're well rid, son," Mrs Petrie said, patting Douglas's shoulder. "I'm calling off the Christmas party. I can't say merry Christmas to that woman!"

"You can't disappoint all those folk on my account," Douglas asserted. "I'll stay away from the party to make things easier for you."

Snow Heaven

TRILLIONS of snowflakes
Tumbling to the ground,
The sheer magic heaven
Spreading all around.
A brilliant white carpet
Comes fitted wall to wall
With serenity and softness
And snow-clad fir trees tall.
The rooftops all a-snuggle
In icy feather down,
The red gold of the lamplight
In the windows round the town.
The cheerful kindly faces
And children chilling out,
All the world's dressed up for Christmas
Now that Santa is about.

Dorothy McGregor.

But despite the marked coolness between Mrs McCracken and Mrs Petrie the tenement party turned out to be a huge success.

Piped music from the Armitages' music centre, stationed just inside their open door, filled the entire building, and everyone sang along with gusto.

Food had been laid out in every flat and Poppy and Colin had organised games for the children. And, of course, there was Santa, who, instead of coming down a chimney or along the street on a reindeer-drawn sledge, emerged from Mr Petrie's shed carrying a sack of gifts.

Poppy and Miss Telford had set up a Santa's grotto on the first landing, with a small artificial Christmas tree and cotton-wool snow and a kitchen chair skilfully disguised as a Santa throne.

Here, the man of the moment held court, handing out the gifts and "ho-ho-ho-ing" behind his magnificent white whiskers.

"Is there not still a wee one to come?" he asked when the last of the children skipped nimbly from his lap and went scooting off up the stairs with his present clutched to his chest. "My elves told me that there was one more and I've another present here."

The women crowded about him looked at each other, puzzled. All the tenement children had been accounted for.

"There's wee Donna Jardine," Miss Telford piped up.

"That must be the one." From his sack, Santa drew a small teddy bear with a red ribbon about its neck. "Where is she?"

'I'm not coming out!' Tricia hissed.

"Well, give me the bairn and I'll take her," her mother said. "Mr Petrie must be desperate to get out of that outfit."

When Donna had been kissed and cuddled and handed back to Poppy, Santa announced, "And now a kiss for the wee one's mummy."

Mrs McCracken backed away.

"You know full well that I'm not her mother!"

"You're not? Well, then," Santa said, "you can pass it on the next time you see her."

Before Mrs McCracken could say another word he'd swept her into his arms.

"Merry Christmas to you and yours," Santa said when he finally released Mrs McCracken. "Merry Christmas, everyone!"

"I thought we were all going to get a wee kiss," Poppy said, disappointed.

* * * *

"You look – different," Tricia said when her mother burst into the flat.

"Here, hold the wean." Mrs McCracken thrust Donna into her daughter's arms and rushed through to the kitchen, where she sat down heavily in her usual chair, across the fire from her husband. He was asleep, a paper hat clinging over one ear and his new Christmas slippers thrust close to the gas radiants.

His wife took hold of both his ankles and eased his feet down on to the floor. He woke with a start.

"It's all right, George – pet," she said, her voice softer than usual. "I was just looking after you." She leaned over and patted his knee.

He eyed her suspiciously, and so did Tricia, standing in the doorway. Something had happened.

Instinctively, Tricia glanced at her mother's feet. Clad in her best black court shoes as they were, it was difficult to tell, but even so it seemed to Tricia that the toes within the smart shiny black exteriors were curling, possibly for the first time in their lives. She turned and slipped quietly from the house.

* * * *

In the shed, Santa unbelted his red coat and hauled out the pillow that had been strapped inside it. As the door handle turned he backed into a darkish corner.

"I knew it was you!"

"Ho, ho, ho!"

"Ho ho nothing, Douglas Jardine," Tricia said, coming in and shutting the door behind her. "You kissed my mother, didn't you?"

'Aye. I don't know why I did it – just a daft idea. Losing you and wee Donna must be affecting my brain."

"You weren't even supposed to be here today. I thought you were going to stay away."

"I couldn't let Christmas pass without seeing the two of you," Douglas protested. "Can I – can I hold her for a minute?"

Tricia passed the baby over.

"I suppose I should say thanks for the teddy," Tricia said awkwardly. "I didn't get anything for you because I was so angry with you."

"I'd settle for you and the wee one coming home with me, where you belong. Look, Tricia, I really can't afford that eternity ring, but as soon as I get my degree and find a decent job you can choose the best, most expensive ring you want."

Wee Donna began to get restless and Tricia took her from Douglas and settled her against the cushion on the deckchair.

"I don't know why I said I wanted it – I was daft! What I really want is you and me and wee Donna being together for always."

Douglas dipped a hand into the pocket of the red coat and brought out a strand of silver tinsel.

"When I get my degree, I'm going to celebrate by buying you that eternity ring, and here's my promise."

He took Tricia's left hand in his and carefully twisted the tinsel round the third finger, above the plain gold wedding ring and the engagement ring with its tiny, tiny diamond.

"Oh, Douglas . . ." she began, then as something rustled in a dark corner she yelped and threw herself at him. "What's that? It's a rat, isn't it? Or a mouse?" She wrapped her arms tightly about him, her face against his. "I hate mice and rats!"

"Suddenly, I quite like them," Douglas said. Then he kissed her, while Donna, her attention caught by the glitter of the tinsel eternity ring against the red of Santa's coat, blinked and smiled.

Now, think about this. That little family could just as easily have been in a stable as a garden shed. And they might have been watched over by sheep and cattle instead of a mouse.

And instead of a wee girl holding out chubby fingers towards a tinsel ring it could have been a little boy reaching towards a star hanging in the sky overhead.

Why couldn't it have been three wise men bringing gifts through the back court, instead of Mr Petrie bearing sandwiches and mince-pies and a flask of coffee?

Why not? Although the years pass, the important things never change. The same things can happen in Bethlehem and in an ordinary Scottish tenement. And sometimes, they do. ■

Portnahaven, Islay

THE picturesque village of Portnahaven on Islay, the most southerly island in the Inner Hebrides, has a sheltered harbour popular with grey seals, which can often be spotted sunbathing on the rocks.

The Gaelic name Port na h-Abhainne means river port, and fishing and crofting provide the main employment.

It's a perfect location for walking, and whether you're an enthusiast or are simply planning a family walk with young children, you're sure to find one graded to match your needs.

Not far from Portnahaven are the Frenchman's Rocks, so called after a French squadron of three ships which were driven on to the rocks by three British frigates in 1760 – not the only ships to come a cropper here.

The crashing waves are also perfect for the commercial wave-powered generation station built near Portnahaven, a world first!.

A trip to Islay wouldn't be complete without a visit to a whisky distillery and having a dram of the "water of life". ∎

174